JACK McAFGHAN's

THE LIZARD
FROM
RAINBOW BRIDGE

A True Tale of an Unexpected Angel

Told by Jack McAfghan
To Kate McGahan

I dedicate this book to all the angels and spirit guides who serve each and every one of us every day. I share this story, hoping to bring people to the light of the knowledge that magic exists everywhere in the world and that the end of this life is not the end of life at all.

"The Rainbow Bridge takes you
to a very real world
beyond what you can see.
It is more real than the world
you think you live in."
- Jack McAfghan

Prologue from Jack

You may have met me in my first book, "Jack McAfghan: Reflections on Life with my Master." In that book, I shared with you my journey with my best friend, Kate. We explored a beautiful life together and we shared with our readers my passage to Rainbow Bridge and how I helped Kate to move through her grief.
In that book I shared the story of many special friends who appeared along the way at the right time and in the right place.
Lizard was one of them.
This story is completely true. It is about a special friend who was much more important than he appeared to be when first we met and he continues to be important to me to this day,
Here on the other side of Rainbow Bridge.

Dear Reader,

Going back hundreds of years in Native American lore, there is said to be a bridge that connects Heaven and Earth. It is called Rainbow Bridge. When we die, we cross this bridge and ultimately find that all the animals we ever encountered during our time on earth are waiting for us there. Little do we know our fate is in their hands. When we cross the bridge to the other side, the animals decide together whether or not to allow us into Heaven. Their decision is based on how we treated them when we shared our time on earth together.

Parts of the story were lost over the ages. Rainbow Bridge and animals have been associated for so long that now it is believed that only animals cross the Rainbow Bridge; that somehow humans take a more direct course from life on earth into Heaven. This is not so.

At an unknown time awhile back, an unknown author wrote a poem called "Rainbow Bridge." This poem is in the public domain and has become a sentimental treasure to people the world over. For those who have lost a best friend, it brings comfort and the reassurance that we will meet again when we too cross the bridge.

In the meantime, when animals in the wild and domesticated pets cross your path, be sure to treat them with love and respect, for they are the ones who will ultimately grant you access to Heaven.

Bless everyone who loves the animals. We look forward to seeing you on the other side of Rainbow Bridge.

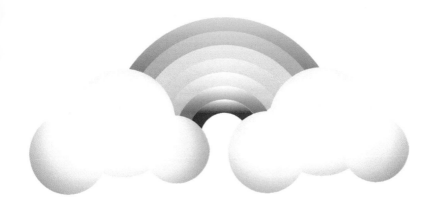

RAINBOW BRIDGE

Just this side of heaven is a place called
Rainbow Bridge.
When an animal dies that has been especially
close to someone here, that pet goes to Rainbow
Bridge.
There are meadows and hills for all of our
special friends
so they can run and play together.
There is plenty of food, water and sunshine,
and our friends are warm and comfortable.
All the animals who had been ill and old are
restored to health and vigor. Those who were
hurt or maimed are made whole and strong
again, just as we remember them
in our dreams of days and times gone by.

The animals are happy and content, except for one small thing; they each miss someone very special to them,
who had to be left behind.
They all run and play together, but the day comes when one suddenly stops and looks into the distance. His bright eyes are intent. His eager body quivers.

Suddenly
he begins to run from the group,
flying over the green grass,
his legs carrying him faster and faster.
You have been spotted, and when you and your special friend finally meet, you cling together in joyous reunion, never to be parted again. The happy kisses rain upon your face; your hands again caress the beloved head, and you look once more into the trusting eyes of your pet, so long gone from your life
but never absent from your heart.

Then you cross Rainbow Bridge together.

I remember the first time I saw him. He was hanging out at the front door of our friend Jane's house around the time her husband went into the hospice. Kate and Jane usually had a lot of fun together, but this day everything seemed to be quite serious and somber. While they sat on the porch discussing the details of life and death, I was getting to know the lizard on the wall.

Lizard was the biggest, coolest-looking lizard I had ever seen, and I've seen a lot of them. I've always enjoyed chasing lizards relentlessly, but this one seemed to command my deepest respect. He was very intelligent and was also full of great wisdom. He was different from the others; I wasn't sure why.

The very next day, we learned that Jane's husband had died during the night. That evening when we went to visit her, we brought her some dinner and a whole lot of compassion. Lizard welcomed us back again. He was still hanging out on the stucco wall above Jane's front door.

"Hello Mr. Lizard!" We greeted him cheerfully.

I wanted to stay outside and talk with him. I hesitated, looking back at him longingly, as Kate ushered me into the house. I obediently went inside with Kate, who then closed the door between Lizard and me.

She and Jane were crying and blowing their noses and wiping their eyes. I don't know why they needed me inside with them; they didn't pay a bit of attention to me. They were consumed with planning the funeral and other things.

All the while I was thinking about Lizard. I lay right there alongside the front door, as close as I could get to him, until it was time to leave. I was glad to see that he was still there when we went back outside.

"See you tomorrow, Mr. Lizard," Kate said to him.

It was fun saying hello and goodbye to him. It was kind of like a game. Even Jane found him fascinating, the way he sat on the wall within arm's length just looking at us, when most lizards would have run away. He seemed fearless. Confident. Strong. Stable. It made me feel confident and strong too, to have him near me. I wanted to be more like him. I wanted to spend more time with him and get to know him.

The next day, we went back to see how Jane was doing. I was disappointed to find that Lizard was gone. I don't think anyone else even missed him. Some people often don't notice when something is missing because when something is out of sight it is out of their mind too, but I was deeply affected. Sometimes you meet someone for the first time and within moments you feel that they are your friend. It's hard to explain, but I missed him. Lizard. He had been there continuously for several days. I wondered where he went.

I learned somewhere along the way that you can make something happen just by thinking positively about it. So I kept thinking about him and it made me happy.

Friends come and friends go, but Lizard is a true forever friend, I know. I just knew that I would see him again somewhere, someday. It's the feeling you get in your heart when you meet someone you know you knew before but you can't remember where it is that you know them from.

It's the spark of love's memory inside your heart that recognizes them and most of the time they recognize you too. That spark is the magnet that always brings us back to each other. Like glue, it binds us together with an invisible cord from lifetime to lifetime, soul mate to soul mate. If two souls are meant to come together in a lifetime, the Universe will conspire to bring the two together as one at the right time and in the right place. No exception.

Every once in awhile I would catch a glimpse of what I thought to be Lizard at our house. Maybe it was just wishful thinking, but we lived right around the corner from Jane, so it would have been quite easy for him to get to our house from hers.

We always had a lot of lizards that came to visit us. It can be hard to tell them apart because many lizards look a lot alike and there are hundreds of them running around at any given time. I'm sure one of the reasons they specifically came to our house was because my sheltie sister Grady and I lived in the neighborhood and we were always up for a good game of Tag or Hide And Seek. I'm sure they liked playing with Grady and me because we never ever caught any of them. We just played the game. We would give them a good run and we'd all be breathless and satisfied by the end of it.

The lizards that came to play with us learned to trust us and they always knew that they were safe from harm. Some animals, the ones who aren't very evolved, can forget that it's just a fun game and they can end up hurting each other. Humans do that too, when they forget that life on earth is for fun and entertainment. Many people can end up taking things so seriously that they spend most of their lives hurting each other. There are also some unfortunate animals that are trained by humans to hunt and to kill for the sport of it. It may be fun for them, but it takes the fun out of it for everyone else.

Not everyone knows this, but many lizards, like many other animals, are angels in disguise. They are everywhere but you can't see most of them. In fact, the harder you try to find them, the harder it is to see them. When you do see them, they come in a flash and then they are gone. They move silent and fast and they leave you stupefied, wondering if you really saw one at all or if you just imagined it. They are little fleeting glimpses of Heaven and they are around us all the time.

Eventually I learned to see the differences in the lizards. It's mostly in their personalities. Just like the rest of us, some of them are outgoing and some of them are shy. Some of them are really fun and some are just plain lazy. If you pay close attention, you learn to recognize them after awhile.

There was an emerald turquoise one that kept coming around. I thought he might be Lizard. He would hang out on our sidewalks and on our walls and we would all play until the sun went down.

I finally figured out that he was a different lizard. He only looked like Lizard. My friend Lizard had a different kind of personality than the rest of them. He was more serious. Lizard wasn't big on playing games. He didn't seem to have a mind for small talk. He wasn't one to waste his energy jumping from one thing to the next. Lizard. He was an interesting guy. He was so different from all the others.

The next time I saw Lizard, I knew without a doubt that he was who I thought he was. I knew him in the first moment. When you don't question something and you know in your heart that it's true, it's like love. If you have to ask yourself if you love someone, you probably don't. You can make it very complicated because even though you know in your heart that it's true, you don't always consult with your heart because your head wants you to think that it's always right, but your head can confuse you. The heart is the one that's always right. I learned this at a very young age and I am glad that I did. It made my life much easier as I went along, to be able to see the truth about things.

This particular day, Lizard showed up at our house. It was a hot day in early summer. He just sat silent and motionless on the wall over Grady's outdoor bed just above our heads.

We had made a special bed for Grady on the front porch. We brought out her favorite blanket and placed it next to the front door. She was sick and we wanted her to be able to stay outside where she always loved to sit, watching the birds and the bugs and the wind in the trees and smelling the natural aromas on the incoming breeze.

Grady was an expert Lizard Vigilante, but because she was so tired this particular day, she wasn't really paying much attention to anything. Here was Lizard five feet above her head and she had no idea he was there. She didn't see him. She didn't smell him. She didn't seem to care. She was sleeping most of the time in those days.

Landscaping our big yard, Kate and I worked long and hard that day. We would always stay within view of Grady. We worried about her and kept a close eye on her. I would run over every so often to check on her. I was so involved with her that I never noticed Lizard there either.

When Kate and I came back to the house at the end of the day, we climbed up the front steps from the lower yard and there he was, sitting on the wall just above Grady's head, staring at us. He had apparently been waiting all day for us to notice him.

"Good Afternoon, Mr. Lizard," said Kate.

I don't think she realized that he was THE Mr. Lizard.

He blinked his eyes at her. Then he looked at me intently as if he was trying to tell me something. I wasn't sure what it was, but I knew that it was something important.

Lizard stayed there with us for several days. He never left his station on the wall above Grady's bed.

On the third day of his visit, we took Grady to the vet. It was the day we came back without her. Kate and I were kind of preoccupied with what had happened that morning, sending Grady off to Rainbow Bridge and all. I think that when we arrived home that day we must have walked right by him and never noticed him. Sometimes we are so blinded by grief that we can't see what's right in front of us.

Later that night when we went out to clear Grady's bed off the porch, there he was, in the same position, still clinging to the wall beside the light. His eyes were closed. He was not there long, for by morning he was gone.

Lizard came to us from out of the blue one day some time later. I was quite surprised when I looked to see him clinging to our screen door. He was jumping around very noisily on the screen hoping that I would notice him.

I recognized him right away. He had a presence that no other lizard possessed. I wondered if he knew who I was because I looked so different. After all, a long time had passed and I had grown from a puppy into a dog and I was twice as big as I was the last time I saw him.

Yes, he said, he knew me. That's why he was at our house. He came to visit me. He said my blonde shaggy hair helped him to identify me, but that I had a personality he could never forget. He told me that wherever I am and wherever I go he will always find me there. He told me that he is never far away.

He sat quietly and talked with me for a long time. He told me very calmly of the great adventures he had experienced in the National Forest that surrounded our village. He had traveled many miles since he had seen us at Jane's house that day and he said that every once in awhile he would think of us. He always knew that he would come back to visit us again. I was happy to learn that I was special to him too, like he was special to me.

He somehow knew that I thought about him a lot. He said that my thinking about him made him think about me. I wondered if his thinking about me made me think about him too, but I was a little too perplexed to ask. He pointed out how we can often forget about some of the others, but certain friends we never ever forget. When a friend suddenly comes to mind for no apparent reason, he said it's because they are near to us in thought or spirit. He explained that a connection takes place on the thought waves that run between us. Thoughts are things

11

that can reach out and touch us. Just thinking about something can make it happen – for better or for worse.

Oh Mr. Lizard! He is a wise and wonderful being. I guess this is the reason why I love him so much. I told him this, but he didn't say "I Love You" back. He just said, "Thank you Jack."

Before he left, he made sure to tell me to keep special watch over Kate in the days ahead. I told him that I would, for I have always been devoted to her. He reminded me to be sure to run right back to the house when the coyotes come around. Of course I already knew to do that too, but it was endearing to me that he was so protective of us. I told him I appreciated him. I told him again that I loved him.

As he was leaving, he looked back at me. I'll never forget the look in his eyes. It was love that went straight into my heart.

Days passed -- maybe even years. Occasionally I'd think about Lizard. There are many shallow friends in the world, full of niceties and sweetness, but Lizard was stimulating to my mind and my heart. He was worldly and seemed to understand many things. I was fascinated by him.

It may sound strange, but he was familiar to me from the very first moment I saw him. He informed me that we knew each other from a long time ago. I couldn't seem to grasp it. It was vague, like a dream you can't quite remember. When you have this kind of feeling about someone, it usually means that you either knew each other before or you have something important to learn from them now. Sometimes it's both.

Lizard helped me to understand that God designs us to be attracted to our teachers. He wants us to love them because when we love someone we want to spend time with them, even if we don't know why we love them or why we want to be with them. Teachers of many different kinds will cross our paths and He creates the circumstances at the right place and at the appointed time to attract us to those that will best teach us the specific lessons we need to learn.

As I have said, I did not know how I knew Lizard; who he was to me before, if I even knew him before. He felt like my father, my brother, my son, my friend... there were times he felt like my mother! He felt like everything all wrapped up into one package. He told me that I could trust him and I knew that it was true. Like a respected guide, I turned to him for help and support. He felt like love. There were quite a few times when he even felt like God.

You always know when you are in the presence of someone special for when you are, you are inspired to think and speak from the very depths of your soul, which can be found at the very bottom of your heart. The soul records and remembers every word you have said and every feeling you have felt from every lifetime you have lived. Often, during certain lifetimes, our minds forget. We're not quite sure how we know them. We recognize the soul light shining in their eyes or we speak to each other from familiar depths. We keep living and learning from them over and over again. We're not supposed to remember all the details of our past life history. God designed it so that we forget each other so that we can have the joy of remembering each other. He gives us just enough to keep us really interested in each other. It's a fun game for Him as lifetime by lifetime we learn to love and be loved more and more...until we become just like Him.

I think Kate really liked Lizard too, even though she and I never talked about him. All she ever said to him was "Hello Mr. Lizard," and "Bye Mr. Lizard." She never said hi to any of the other lizards so maybe she realized that he was a special lizard too. I don't know.

I would always wonder where Lizard went when he wasn't around. It was like something was missing when he was somewhere else. It was weird because I had never felt like anything was missing in my life until I met him.

Winter was behind us. Spring had finally arrived and we were starting to leave the windows and doors open to invite the fresh air into the house. Spring is the time of year for the survivors of the winter season to get busy living life again.

Once in awhile we might leave a door open for a moment too long and visitors would come right into the house; crickets, flies, bees, sometimes a bird or other things with wings. She would talk to them and patiently usher them back outside. She always said she loved all things, but she told me that those who needed to be outdoors needed to stay outdoors.

One quiet morning, when we weren't paying attention, Lizard came back. He came right into our house through a little hole in the screened patio door. I saw him come in and my heart leaped with joy to see him again. Like a man on a mission, he seemed to know right where he was headed. He ran straight for the fireplace hearth, where he scurried up the rough surface with his sure-webbed feet and then he just sat there, like a decoration that you would find in a southwest novelty shop. I hoped that Kate might let him stay with us when she saw him.

"Well hello Mr. Lizard. What on Earth are YOU doing here?"

For some reason she felt she couldn't just leave him there on our hearth, I didn't know why. I think she read my mind because she looked over at me then and reminded me that Lizard had to go back outside where he belonged.

She spoke to him in a calm voice while she carefully pulled his webbed feet off the cinder blocks, cradled him in a soft towel and carried him outside, where they sat for a little while talking. I don't know what they were talking about because I went back out to the kitchen to finish my breakfast and drink some water. When I returned, Kate was inside getting dressed for work and Lizard was still sitting on the towel on the bench.

Kate went to work and Lizard stayed in the same place on that towel on the bench for many hours. I think he fell asleep there; I'm not sure. Then he left. I don't know where he went or why he left, but I knew that he would be back because he told me that he would be. He told me he would come back to see me in a few months. I liked that thought. I liked knowing that I could be sure of seeing him again.

Several months passed and I wasn't feeling too well. Kate had scheduled an appointment for me at the vet clinic the first day of that week. As we were going out the door on the way to the clinic, there he was! Lizard had come back. Kate noticed him too. He was hanging on the wall near the light by our front door near the bench. He was in the same place and in the same position that he was in when we first saw him hanging over Grady's makeshift bed that day when I was a pup.

"Well if it isn't Mr. Lizard!" she exclaimed, "How are you? Where have you been hiding?"

Of course he didn't answer her, but he was communicating all the while with me. I didn't have to say anything. He knew I was going to the vet and he wished me well.

When we came back he was still there. It was so much fun to have him at our house again! I sat outside the front door and he sat above me by the light and we just hung out together. He commented on the recent changes in the weather; monsoons were fast approaching. He was making plans for where he would stay, protected from the floods and rushing waters that typically come to our area in the summertime.

I told him that he was more than welcome to stay forever with us under the light under the eave of the roof, but he just said no; he couldn't stay with us for too long. He told me he had a job to do and that he had to go to some other places, but that his place this particular week was with me, with us, at our house. He said today is Monday, tomorrow is Tuesday and that he would be staying until Friday night.

I was glad he would be staying for a while. I told him how special I thought he was; that he most certainly must be my teacher, but that he felt like a soul mate too.

He said yes, we are most definitely soul mates. He told me that soul mates come into our lives at very precise times to inspire and to awaken us to bigger and better ways of looking at the world and interacting with it. We've known each other before, he said, and we will know each other again. He had told me this before, but it was finally making sense to me. He informed me that we both belong to a certain soul group that carries an extra strong bond. He explained that a soul group is like a special family.

He told me that if anything ever happened to me, not to worry. He would be there with me if ever I need him and that he will also keep special watch over Kate, for she is in our soul family too.

The next morning Lizard watched us leave again from his station near the porch light, but he didn't say anything. He just watched us.

Kate said "Good morning, Mr. Lizard," as we passed by. She told him we were going back to the vet clinic.

He didn't answer. He didn't say anything, but he looked at me so intently that I will never forget, even if I live a thousand lifetimes, the look in his eye. It was care, concern and a deep and pervasive love beyond the likes of which I have never known.

I didn't know then what was going to happen. There were a lot of things I didn't know yet. I'm still a little confused about it, but I had some kind of surgery and was very weak and in a lot of pain. I couldn't do much when we got home that day. I wasn't thinking straight.

Lizard was waiting for us. He was looking at me but he wasn't saying anything. He must've known I was in bad shape. Tuesday came and went. Wednesday. Thursday. I was getting worse and worse.

Every once in awhile she would leave my side and go out and talk with him. She would smile softly at him like he was an old friend, for he was, and then she would give him the sad report of how I was doing.

The time came when she cried to him because she knew it was inevitable that I was leaving this place. She asked him if he knew of anyone who could help us. In her heart she knew it was out of her hands but her head was still trying to find a solution. When she couldn't find a solution, she started looking for a miracle. She asked the only one who was available and near. She asked Lizard.

She couldn't hear him answer her but I could, even though I was on the kitchen floor on the far side of the house.

"I'm here for you," he said to her. "I'm here for Jack. I'll make sure everything's okay."

Even though she couldn't hear him I think she picked up on his message deep inside her heart. She somehow felt better having talked with him.

In the early hours of Friday morning before dawn, I crossed over Rainbow Bridge. Lizard came to me during the final hours when I was sleeping. Our angels often come to us in the times when we are unconscious because those are the times we are free of the continual thoughts of our mind. It is here that we remember who we really are. We remember who we are in our soul. We are greater than the physical life we have been living on earth. It was here that I remembered how I knew Lizard and all the reasons why I loved him. I remembered all the lives we had shared together. Oh I remembered everything! He could speak directly to my soul and I could hear him clearly.

He told me what to expect. He told me that he would guide me over Rainbow Bridge and he prepared me for what would happen on the other side. He told me that there would be others crossing over with me and he was right. There were many others! He made my crossing much easier by showing me the way and preparing me ahead of time. I learned that all who cross Rainbow Bridge have a familiar escort to guide and comfort them on their journey.

All this was going on and yet in the back of my mind I was worried about what would happen to Kate after I was gone.

"Don't worry," Lizard reassured me, "I promise to stay with her and make sure she's okay too, before I leave."

This reassurance from him was all I needed to let go and fly free to the bridge. It was a glorious feeling to fly, unshackled from the pain and suffering I had come to know. Such relief came to me as I felt my burdens melting away. They were replaced with the comfort of knowing that perfect love was waiting for me on the other side. All the love I gave and more. Waiting there for me.

I could hear in the far recesses of my mind her voice saying, "Go Home little boy. Go Home. Fly free!"

I flew to Rainbow Bridge on the wings of my love for her.

When I arrived, I was surrounded by all the love I ever gave in all my lifetimes put together. It was beyond description the beauty and peace of it all. I was so excited because I knew that one day she would be coming Home to me and that all the love she gave, and more, would be waiting here for her. I couldn't wait for her to feel all that heavenly love surround her too. I would be patient, however, for time is just an illusion. I knew that it would all happen in the blink of eye, the way things do.

That afternoon she went out to the porch and, sure enough, Lizard was there just like he told me he would be. She sat down on the bench. She had learned to trust him and she felt that she could be herself with him. She cried and cried. She also made some silly jokes and her shaky laughter broke the tension of her sadness, somewhat. He laughed gently with her, telling her that humor is just a cover up for the anger and depression that so often come when you deeply grieve the loss of someone you love.

She thanked Lizard for being there for us.

"I know you understand," she said to him. "I don't know how I know this, but I know that you do. Thank you. Thank you. Thank you for loving Jack too."

Later that night she went out to see him again but he was nowhere to be found. He had not moved from the wall by the door for five whole days and now he was gone.

It was Friday.

She arose the next day after a sleepless night. It had been raining all week and it seemed fitting given the overcast state of mind she was in. Missing me to no end, she put on her raincoat to venture out into the storm. People can do funny things when they grieve.

She opened the front door and in her loneliness she looked for Mr. Lizard, to no avail, and went on her way through the pouring rain to walk our trail through the nearby woods.

The trail was rushing with mud and water but she didn't care. She cried as the heavy rains joined her wet face until she didn't know where the tears ended and the rain began. She was pleading with me along the way; looking everywhere for me.

"Jack. Jack where are you?"

I saw her. I heard her. It made me unhappy to see her so sad but there was not yet anything I could do about it. I had not yet finished my trek over Rainbow Bridge. You can't come back from someplace if you haven't arrived there yet.

A little while later, she reached the end of our trail and made her way back to our house. It loomed ahead of her like a stranger. It screamed to her how empty it was. She didn't know what to expect of herself when she opened the door. She was so focused on her anxiety about the

25

house that she never looked back at our path.
She never looked behind her. She never knew
there was a tiny ray of sunshine peeking
through the dark clouds above the mesa. It was
a ray of sunshine just for her. Had she turned
around, she would have seen the rainbow there.

The rainbow was my sign to her to let her know
that all was well. I had made my passage safely.
I learned that we are never apart. I was sorry
she missed it. It was time to learn how to
connect with her from beyond Rainbow Bridge.

Soaked to the skin, she was pleasantly
surprised to find Lizard had returned to his
appointed place on the wall beneath the light. I
was kind of surprised too because he had told
me that he would be there with her until Friday,
but now it was Saturday. I thought maybe he
had fallen in love with her too and just wanted
to be with her.

"Oh am I glad to see you Mr. Lizard."

She sat down on the bench under the eave with him while the rain continued to come down in torrents around them. They sat together for a long time and talked. They talked about me. They talked about loss. They talked about death. They talked about life. They talked about love. They talked about Heaven and the Rainbow Bridge and they talked about God.

She didn't know that Lizard had left her just long enough between dusk and dawn to escort me to the Rainbow Bridge. He wasn't about to tell her. Lizard was honest and open, but he wasn't allowed to speak of certain things. There is a rule in Heaven that says we cannot tell someone something that might shift the living out of their destiny during their lifetime on earth. People must be led by either their mistakes or by their faith, and this is why they cannot be told certain things ahead of time.

Still, I could not help but wonder. Why did Lizard go back to her?

She was preparing to go inside. She asked him if he needed anything but he said no. He never needs or wants for anything. He thought it was sweet that she had left the light on for him the night before, but he wasn't into eating bugs. That's not why he was there.

She took off her wet boots and coat and left them there on the bench before going inside. It was time for her to start getting used to the house without me there.

The house had always been her friend but now she had a dark sense of foreboding as she walked through the door. She wasn't prepared for the sadness and the pain of it all. She focused on the little things. She lived in each and every moment, trying to feel feelings that were numbed by her grief. She walked the hallways, staring vacantly, as if she had never seen our house before. Her mind was vague and hazy for grief can be like a drug that dulls the senses. It seemed a strange world to her now; far from the familiar home that she and I had shared together.

She thought it was a bit strange that she wasn't crying, especially considering how she always felt she would not know how to live her life without me. She thought it would be the hardest thing ever, and yet in this moment it seemed that she was doing just fine.

"Wow," she said out loud to the empty house, "I thought I would be so upset and I'm really feeling okay."

She didn't realize then that she was in a state of shock and denial. She knew in her heart what had happened, but it hadn't registered in her head yet, my departure from life as we knew it. She also had been too busy with the details surrounding my passing for the reality of it all to sink in.

I watched her enter our bedroom. This was the place that was always our safe haven, far from the demands and troubles of the world. It was the closest thing to heaven on earth for us. She took a deep breath and sat stiffly on the edge of our bed. She felt somehow like she was in a movie, like her life wasn't real.

"What am I supposed to do now?"

With shaky fingers she traced the patterns in my butterfly blanket, over and over again. It was a strange activity that made her feel like she could rely on something, riding along the quilted curves of the pastel butterflies. Meanwhile she looked around the empty room. She kept picturing me there.

"Dear God, what is it that I should be doing?"

She was very good at rationalizing things. Most people are. It makes them think that they are in control of something when they really aren't.

Her mind got hazy. She seemed trapped between her memories and reality. For just a moment she thought she saw me there on my blanket on the bed. She reached over to touch me and as she did she shook her head to clear her mind, as if to process what was happening. As she focused in the moment, she found that she touched only air. If only she could have stayed in the space between her memory and reality, she might have actually touched me. We were so close and yet so far. Still, I felt happy, for she had seen me there. For that moment I pierced the veil between earth and Rainbow Bridge. She saw me there. She saw me!

She suddenly became overwhelmed in the moment when she thought I disappeared. She was stricken with helplessness. She wanted me back. She wanted to touch me for real. She didn't know what to do because it is not every day that someone you love dies. She reached over and drew my butterfly blanket close to her and then her grief seized her quickly and without warning.

Muffling her sobs into the softness of my blanket, she broke down and cried. It would be the beginning of a million tears.

Somehow when I talked to Lizard he would hear my voice but when I talked to her she couldn't hear me. I had so much to learn. She had so much to learn. Lizard was here to help both of us. He was our bridge to each other.

The rain continued to batter the world outside but inside she was finally calm, albeit exhausted from her crying. In her travels through the house, she found a little toy bottle of soap bubbles and was blowing them around in every room. I never saw her do that before. I think she just had a lot of nervous energy and she had to do something, anything, to diffuse it. She blew most of the bubbles onto my favorite places – on the bed, on the couch, along the front door where I used to watch over her like a sentry. She blew them all over my butterfly blanket. I wonder if she saw the rainbows I put into the bubbles for her ...and for me.

Later she was holding my collar in her hands, sitting on my favorite place on the sofa. She seemed to be under a spell. She was jolted back to reality when the phone rang. She took the call. She was now ready to share what had happened to me with someone who cared. She wasn't sure how she'd put it into words, but she was ready. It was her father who was calling.

She answered wearily with feigned cheerfulness and was taken by surprise. It was not her father on the other end of the phone at all, but some people who were using his phone to tell her that he had died unexpectedly, perhaps in his sleep, the night before. They weren't sure what time. It was within a few hours of my passing. They were there with him. She needed to leave immediately.

Shocked, she had hardly come to terms with my death and now she was facing another. She was very glad that Lizard was there outside her door. He brought with him a measure of comfort and she felt less alone in her grief and her ever-growing despair.

It was reassuring for me as well that Lizard was there with her. He was a stable presence. It seems he took over my position as her protector, never moving from his post outside the front door. He stayed there for the three days it took her to take care of her father's apartment and to pack up his things.

While she was taking care of his affairs, I was escorting him across the Rainbow Bridge. Lizard brought him to me. I was glad that I knew where to go and what to do so that I could show him the way.

It is all by design why things happen the way they do. I had to leave first so that I could know what to expect, so that I could then lead her father there too. I was the chosen one. God knew that he'd put his trust in me.

On the third day she brought in some big boxes from her car. As she struggled with carrying them into the house, she looked up and found that Lizard was there to welcome her home.

"Hi Mr. Lizard."

She was totally exhausted. She wanted to sit down with him later and she told him this. She brought a cup of tea out with her in the evening and sat on the bench and talked with him for a very long time. Mostly she thanked him for being there when she needed someone. She appreciated him for helping to fill the empty space in her life that had been filled with me and that had been filled with her father. In her heart she was hoping that Lizard would stay forever under the light on the stucco wall outside the door. Perhaps she was falling in love with him too.

The next day she was especially sad because, not only was I gone and her father gone, but Lizard was gone too. Well, we weren't really "gone" but she couldn't see us. Lizard told me that he had to leave on another assignment. He was not sure if he would be back again to see her.

Days, weeks, months passed. The winter was the hardest winter on record. She was grieving and she was healing. Time heals everything if you let it. Still, she thought of me night and day. She thought of her father.

She thought of Lizard often too. She thought of him as the seasons changed and the monsoons washed the summer days away. She would often look longingly over our mesa trail and find herself lost in her memories of me. She would look up there and worry about Lizard too. She thought about him fending for himself. She imagined the predators waiting in the high grasses for him and hungry winter hawks waiting in the trees. She thought of him fighting off the snow and the wind and the cold. She wondered where he was living and she prayed that he was safe and warm. She wondered if he had a family. She hoped that he was loved. She prayed that he was not alone.

I was very glad that she believed in Heaven and the Rainbow Bridge so that she didn't worry about her father and me. She had the faith that there is an end to all pain and suffering in Heaven. She believed that life goes on. She knew that the struggles and discomforts of life on earth could not reach us there. She didn't understand, however, that she didn't need to worry about Lizard either.

All the while Lizard was very busy, fulfilling missions elsewhere. He thought of her now and then. Of course he would, for she was thinking of him too. He was pretty sure that she was upset with him. After all, it is hard to be God's messenger when it's your turn to take someone away from someone who loves them. He hoped that she would forgive him because he knew that forgiveness is one of the most important things on the face of the earth, for the one who forgives as much as for the one forgiven. He was hoping to return to her one day, to ask her forgiveness.

One week early in March, spring finally broke through. Ice was melting on the crystallized creek nearby. The sun returned to warm the earth and the trees and everything that lived there. It awakened the seeds and the bulbs, the birds and the bees. It is the one reliable thing in life. When all else fails, the seasons will change again and again. It is a reminder that everything is in perfect and divine order.

Spring came quickly and easily, as things by design do. It was a sentimental time for her, for as life returned to the world around her, death and loss still raged in her troubled mind. The budding life made her miss us even more.

I was with her all the time. I kept reminding her that life is perennial and that which seems to be dead is always revived and refreshed. Like her father and me, we are very much alive! We are only gone from her sight. While she had made great efforts and was healing little by little from the losses, the fact that she couldn't hear my voice told me that she still had a long way to go. The fact that she couldn't see me or feel me when I was right beside her told me that she did not yet have peace of mind.

She wondered if Lizard was still around. She wondered if the springtime was waking him too.

Her life had become simpler since the passing of her father and me. She was keeping more to herself. The mundane details of life that consumed the conversations of those around her either fell on her deaf ears or drove her to the brink of insanity. She kept most of her thoughts to herself. No one really wanted to hear about her ongoing grief and her sorrow.

People who grieve usually go to one extreme or the other. They will either spend too much time alone in isolation or they will throw themselves into activities in an effort to not think about their loss. It seems like it's productive but it's often an escape from the grief. It delays the healing.

I was glad she chose to be alone. Ultimately she had enough privacy and peace around her to learn to receive my words. It took us many months. I had spoken to her so many times and then one day, to my delight, she heard me. She heard me at last.

Challenged and energized by this, she became totally focused on writing our life story, hers and mine. She only wanted to be with me, to think about me and to work on our book. The book, as far as she was concerned, was our connection, but it was so much more than that. My voice filled her head and she was consumed with filling the pages of our book with what I said. It healed her by her writing of it. It healed me by the way she honored it. It would come to heal both of us by the sharing of it. Little did she know that our book would also come to heal thousands of readers.

Months passed. She had worked long and hard to get our book just right for publication. She was finally ready to share it. One night, having finished proofreading it for the umpteenth time, she was packaging it up to send off to a professional editor. She got into her car, drove to the local post office to mail the manuscript, ran a couple errands, and then returned home. Little did she know, she was supposed to go out at that very time to that very place, for had she not she would have missed what was waiting for her when she arrived home.

Upon her return as she approached the house, she saw something light-colored in the road ahead of her. She brought her car to a stop, squinting at the small form on the pavement through the glow of the headlights.

"Is that what I think it is?"

She jumped out of the car to examine what seemed to be lifeless, splayed out on the hard dark pavement.

It was Lizard. I had been there to witness it all. He was badly injured. He had been crossing the road, heading straight for our house. He had stopped just a few feet away from our garage.

Running into the house, she got some clean towels and tools. When she returned, she carefully pulled his webbed feet off the blacktop, just as she had pulled them off our cinder blocks that first day when she met him face to face. She wasn't sure he could hear her, but she spoke to him in a comforting tone.

She studied him closely. Lizard wasn't moving at all. She couldn't even tell if he was alive. She couldn't see him breathing.

He looked much older. His scales and his body were intact but he was missing an eye. The other side of his face was caved in. It had blood on it and he had blood all around the edges of his mouth. She knew enough about medical situations that if someone bleeds this way, they could have internal injuries that can easily be fatal.

Her tears began to flow. The thought of losing Lizard brought back all the pain and sadness of losing me and her father and Grady too. Each loss tends to bring back all the others for healing.

She was taken by complete surprise when suddenly Lizard, in one swift move, jumped high up onto the right arm of her jacket. One webbed foot clasped the drawstring of her hood while the others grabbed hold of her arm and held on tight. She didn't know quite what to make of it.

She didn't have as much fear as she used to have. She was much calmer these days, so she simply walked into the house with Lizard clinging to her arm. Dinner was in the oven but she turned the oven off and decided to forget about it. She didn't care about anything but Lizard. She didn't really know what to do with him. She went into the living room and sat on the couch and let him cling to her arm for the longest time.

There is a strange intangible place on the outside edges of the human mind. It hangs there like a constant witness. It judges a person's every move, every thought and every action. Some people think it is "big brother" or God, but it is just a critical place inside the person's own mind that judges and condemns. It is the very place where we judge ourselves when we cross Rainbow Bridge into Heaven. People call it "Judgment Day." They think God is there to judge them, but it is not God who judges at all. It is said that the animals make the decision but in reality, the animals only lift up a mirror to the one seeking entry. This is to show them objectively who they are, so that they can decide whether or not they themselves are worthy.

If they feel that they are unworthy, they are given an opportunity to live another life and learn more love in the Earth School. If they are worthy, they can enter through the gates of Heaven if they so desire.

The purpose of life on Earth, after all, is to remove everything but the love in one's soul. Perfect love is all that exists on the other side of Rainbow Bridge, so only those who are the same as the love that lives there can enter. Some of us are so close that by the time we reach the other side of the bridge, the Rainbow itself transforms us the rest of the way.

So here she was with Lizard. She was feeling embarrassed as she looked at herself from the disapproving borderlands of her mind. There was no one there to witness her except her own conscience. She questioned herself.

"What's the matter with you? What on earth would people think if they saw you with a lizard cradled like a baby in your arms in your living room?" Oh how silly it all seemed to be!

But this was not a normal situation and this was not an ordinary lizard. The situation was far from silly. It was very real and it was imperative for her growth and ultimately for the resolution of her grief. It was by Design.

It was getting late. She eventually slid her arm out of the jacket, leaving Lizard still clinging to the drawstring. She decided to sleep on the couch beside him.

During her all-night vigil, he did not seem to be breathing. She was sure that he was dying. All through the night he was silent and still. All through the night she was preparing to bury him on the trail with my ashes in the morning.

Dawn came. He had not moved a muscle. She went to gently lift him off her jacket to place him in the towel to prepare for proper burial, but instead she found, by some miracle, that he was still alive. She took him outside where the morning sun had just begun to warm the front porch.

As soon as the sun shone down upon him, he seemed to come to life. An hour later he was awake and alert. He lifted his head and even took a drop of water from her. His injured eye was swollen and the place where his other eye used to be was caked with blood and dirt.

As the day passed he again became quiet and still. He really did look sickly and pathetic. Once again she prepared for his demise. She slept on the couch beside him and in the morning when she woke, she found him in the very same position she had left him in the night before. He was still breathing.

He was very slow to rouse. This gave her a chance to look closely at his wounds. She cleaned the blood off of him with gentle sprays of water while he continued to sleep, seemingly oblivious. She then saw something thin and pointed coming out of his good eye and it seemed to be an insect stinger or a cactus needle. She got her tweezers and firmly grabbed and pulled. She pulled it straight out. He recoiled and writhed in pain for ten long seconds and then he lay totally still. She was sure that she had killed him.

An hour later the morning sun returned, shining down upon him. Once again he livened up, standing erect and alert. He was obviously feeling better. It was not long and he was walking sluggishly around on her lap as they sat together on the bench outside. She was happy to see him active. She thought he might have a chance at life. There were no more traces of blood on him. The swelling was going down on one side and the wound seemed to be healing on the other.

Lizard never opened his good eye. She wondered if he was blind. She knew he wasn't deaf because he seemed to hear her in the moments when he was alert. He was surprisingly sensitive to her changing moods. When she would fill up with tears or strong emotion, even when she was really quiet about it, he would respond to her instantly, turning his head towards her in an effort to console her. He was very tuned in vibrationally. She never communicated with him quite the way I did, but she and Lizard, they seemed to be coming to some understandings.

She talked to him all the time. She gave him choices. He could stay inside with her. He could go outside. He could leave. He could stay. He could live. He could die. Whatever he wanted, she said, it was okay. She would help in every possible way to see it through. I was proud of her because she was letting go of her need to be needed and loved in exchange for setting him free. It made me happy because she was finally learning about true love; love that is not based on dependence or need.

She spent a lot of time with him. Time that she didn't really have. She desperately wanted to heal him. Part of this went back to her grief and to her relationship with me. She had desperately wanted to heal me too, but she couldn't. It was unfinished business. She didn't know why she was so driven to heal Lizard. In reality she wanted to heal him because she actually needed to heal herself. When we heal someone else, we always heal something inside of ourselves at the same time.

Lizard remained weak and he still couldn't see. He wasn't eating. Once in a great while he would take a drop of water from the eyedropper that she offered to him. Every day she had him outside a little longer than the day before. She knew that he was too weak to fend for himself, so while he was outside she put him in the safest place she could think of. She put him under an upside-down wire basket. We tend to get in return that which we give. Lizard had protected her for so long that he was now getting back that very same protective care from the one he had given it to.

As the days passed, she realized that she needed to resume living her life. She began to feel a sense of urgency. She didn't understand that the urgency she was feeling was his. Lizard had an assignment to complete soon. He needed to be healthy and independent in order to fulfill it.

She was driven to heal him and eager to wean him from her care. She proceeded to learn everything she could possibly learn about rehabilitating lizards. She laid her hands upon him in the hopes of curing him. She used crystal-healing methods and practiced Reiki to infuse him with energy. She asked for help from Mother Mary and all the angels and saints. She tried everything she could think of. Mostly she surrounded him with her warmth and her love. She didn't really need all that other stuff. She just needed her faith and her love to heal him. He could do the rest.

She put a pillow with my photo on it beside him at night so that I could "watch over him" while she slept. She didn't need to do that for I was watching over him anyway, lots of us were, but it made her feel better. People seem to feel better when they can fuss over things. Keeping busy gives them a sense of control when there isn't any.

She had to admit that she had some underlying concerns about why Lizard had found his way back into her life again. She wondered if he was another omen or once again the bearer of bad news... but so far everything seemed to be okay.

Many days passed. Lizard still wasn't eating. She asked around town for help, but no one knew very much about lizards. Some of them thought she was a little eccentric to be taking care of a wild lizard. She ended up at a big metropolitan pet store some distance away where she found some of the answers she was looking for. The guy in the reptile department told her that the most important thing was to keep Lizard warm, especially during his time of recovery.

She wanted to do the right thing for Lizard. She closely followed the expert's recommendations. She bought an aquarium, some live worms and crickets and she set up a little house for him. The pet store guy told her to be careful because if Lizard didn't eat the crickets in a certain amount of time, they would get hungry and would eat him instead.

She found a shallow crystal dish and put a thin layer of water in it so that he would have his own private pond. She didn't use a bowl for she feared that he would drown. A smooth juniper branch helped to create a natural environment, with all of the elements present. She wanted it perfect for him. She read up on lizard nutrition and provided him with organic lettuce and carrots. She put them right near his head in the hopes that he would find them but he didn't touch them.

She would put him outside all day and bring him in at night because it was still very cold after the sun went down. She doted on him. She did for him what she would have wanted done for her if she were a lizard.

She didn't have a clue that she didn't need to worry about any of these things. She didn't understand that there was nothing really that could happen to him; nothing at all that could destroy him. He was not an ordinary lizard. He was a spiritual angel. He was indestructible, but she simply didn't know this. She wasn't supposed to. She was supposed to feel desperate. She was supposed to focus on him because she had something very important to learn from this experience with him.

He spent the first few days in his garden house sleeping in the middle of the shallow pool of water.

The crickets walked all over him -- around his mouth and on top of his head. His good eye was still closed. The worms slowly crept and crawled alongside him. He paid no attention whatsoever to any of them. Kate was watching carefully, with a certain level of discomfort at the thought of the crickets eating Lizard, or even to the other extent, Lizard eating the crickets.

Soon the worms were eating the carrots and then the crickets started eating the worms. She began to feel guilty and sickeningly responsible. The environment she had created for healing was instead leading to the loss of life.

She worried nonstop about the possibility of the crickets eating him, so it wasn't long before she set the crickets free in the side yard, along with the worms. She went back to the store and bought a can of dead crickets and mushed them up in water and fed him bits and pieces with the dropper. It almost made her sick. It's amazing what someone will do for love. He took a little bit of the concoction, but not much. She didn't realize that he was an angel spirit and that angel spirits don't need to eat. They don't have needs like earthbound creatures do. He was just humoring her by taking the cricket drops.

Lizard didn't appear to be benefitting at all from the makeshift restaurant and spa, but he was actually getting stronger every day under her protective care. He was energized by her growing love for him. Most of the time he just stayed under the shade of the juniper branch with his tail hanging out. She couldn't see him under there. She couldn't tell if he was breathing or asleep or awake or alive or dead. She kept worrying that he went under there to die. Her imagination always got the best of her. One's imagination can often be more disturbing than reality. He knew what he was doing. He was teaching her in the space where she couldn't see him, how her own mind worked and how she was her own worst enemy.

Each and every morning she would be delighted that Lizard had not died during the night. It, however, did not seem to her that he was improving either.

They established a routine. She'd put him outside. About an hour after the sun hit his skin, he'd come around. She kept moving Lizard, following the course of the sun as it circled around the house, to keep him awake and alert throughout the day. At night, when it got cool, she'd bring him back into the house. Each night was the same: long nights of not moving. She would watch him intently, looking for signs of life. She couldn't see him breathing. Each night she prepared for his death and the next day would come again; same thing. This happened over and over again.

She put him on pretty fabrics to keep him comfortable, but lizards are not like people. They only get their claws caught in the finely looped strands of the fabric and then they are prisoners of the fabric until someone comes to set them free. So that wasn't working out too well. Then she found a nice flat desert rock and placed it between him and the fabric. He seemed to like the rock. Sometimes she warmed it up in the microwave. He would cling to it like he clung to her arm that very first night.

By day he would seem to improve, but every night he looked like death. Things seemed to be getting worse. His body was bloating, his belly was swelling and his green scales were dropping off leaving brown patches. She didn't know what to do. She couldn't force him to eat. There was nowhere to turn for help. She was hitting a wall. Nothing she did seemed to be working. She felt desperate.

When something comes to you over and over again, it's important to pay attention. Most people notice how they keep repeating the same patterns when they are finally ready to learn and make changes in their lives. She realized that she was burning herself out trying to anticipate and meet his needs. She was tired of her own worries and the tears of frustration that now came each and every night when she thought it would be Lizard's last.

As she looked at Lizard and continued to wonder whether tonight would be the night that he would cross over, she finally realized that whatever the end result, it would be okay. She started to realize that all along she had just been spinning her wheels. Lizard was not of this world at all. The rules of living and dying did not even apply to him.

She started praying for him. She would sing "Amazing Grace" to him, stressing the words 'I once was blind but now I see." At night when she could not see him breathing, she would start singing softly to him and she found that he would always start breathing deeply at the first sound of her voice. She could see his lungs go in and out. If she stopped singing he would stop breathing. He would seem to be at the edge of death, and upon hearing her voice he would prove himself to be very much alive.

He liked that particular song, for it was a song of faith. Out of curiosity she played a recording of a popular country singer singing the same song, but Lizard did not react to that at all. This made her think that he was responding to her voice but he was really teaching her. Teaching her that she could get farther with faith and prayer than she ever could with worry and overthinking. He wanted her to see how healing her own faith could be.

She learned how to heal him and he got better and better. She would sing to him several times a day. He would be sound asleep and then as soon as her voice reached his ears, he would turn around to face her with his good side. By some miracle, his eyesight had returned. He could see again with his good eye and he would look right up at her. To her it looked like he was squinting but I think he was actually smiling. You know, the kind of smile that comes across your face when you can't help but love someone.

When lizards are healthy, they have a very good internal ability to know their way around. Things were looking up. She would move him around, but she always kept him on his favorite flat red rock. He would open his one good eye long enough to look up at her and to see where she was taking him. Mostly he wanted to see that she was there and then he would close it again.

It was all very endearing for her, but the days were passing. Many days. She was getting increasingly restless, as caregivers tend to do at a certain point when they begin to tire and they don't know how much longer someone will need them.

"What is it that you want?" she asked him one morning while he sat staring at her, motionless.

"Did you come to me for help?"

No response.

"Did you come here to die?"

There was no answer.

"Did you come here to tell me something?"

He said yes in response, but she didn't hear him.

"Is there something you want me to do for you?"

YES, he said again.

She sat with him quietly. She was almost as still and as calm as he was. She waited, tuned in to his very being. Hanging on his every breath as he had taught her to do.

Yes, he repeated. Yes, there is something I want you to do for me.

She heard him this time, not through her ears but deep in the knowingness of her heart.

She was finally tuned in to the wavelength that connects all of us. I was so excited because it was the same wavelength that would connect her to me. It was the key to our being together again.

"Okay," she said. "Tell me what you want and I will do it for you."

He told her he wanted her to write his story. He told her that he was a spirit guide, an angel; an animal totem. He told her he was my friend. He was a messenger from heaven and it was his wish to spread his message to everyone upon the earth. He had been working on teaching students one at a time but he knew if she could write a book, that his message could reach more people than he could reach in a thousand lifetimes.

He told her about all the creatures of the earth from each and every species and how they come back into this world to help the others. He was from the Spirit World at Rainbow Bridge and he came here for the express purpose of helping others to cross over the sacred bridge into Heaven.

He shared with her how he helped me to cross over so that I, in turn, could help her father to cross over. He said that she would be crossing over one day too, she and many others. He told her not to be afraid.

He wanted her to share his story so that people would know there is more to a lizard than meets the eye; there is more to everything than there seems at first glance. That there is never any cause for fear.

She told him she would write his story after she finished writing ours.

She was motivated to get Lizard rehabilitated. He needed to get back to doing his good work and she needed to get back to hers.

He still would do very little of his own accord. He would stay wherever she put him. One day she put him on the bench right across from his old favorite spot on the wall by the porch light. She thought maybe he would be tempted to go back up there if he looked at it long enough, but he did not. He didn't even look at it.

One day she took it upon herself to lift him up and place him on the wall. It was a gesture of tough love. She did not want to force him into doing something he was not prepared to do. She knew how that felt and how one feels towards the one who pressures. She was able to set this aside. She did not worry about what he thought of her. She was acting in his best interest. It was all about Lizard. She wanted him to prove to himself that he could once again hang vertical on the wall. She knew that if he could do this that he would start feeling like himself in no time.

As she raised him to the wall, his webbed feet stretched and spread as they met with the rough surface. Soon he was clinging to the stucco as he so often had before.

After she placed him there, she wished him well and left for work. Later when she came home, he had not moved a muscle. He was still clinging to the wall where she had placed him eight hours earlier.

Day after day, she put him on the wall and he would wait on the wall until she took him off. If she put him on the bench he would wait on the bench. It didn't matter where she put him, he would stay there.

She began to wish that he would take some control of himself; take the responsibility off of her shoulders and return to the wild, but many days and weeks passed and nothing changed.

One day she placed him, still on top of his rock, right beside the front entry gate. She told him that he could go if he wanted to. She pointed him in the right direction towards freedom, straight out that gate towards my trail and the National Forest beyond.

Whether he couldn't or whether he wouldn't, Lizard did not leave. It had been nine weeks. He was waiting for her to make the next move.

She was still writing our book, which she wanted to finish before writing Lizard's story. While she was proofreading, she read it aloud to him. It was fun for him to hear the parts that were written about him.

She never saw him eat anything. She didn't know how he could possibly still be alive. She would give him some water from the dropper every day or two. He took it just to make her happy.

One morning when she picked him up, she realized he was vastly improved. His scales were growing back and, despite the lack of food, he was shapely and filling in nicely. He was gaining strength and power. While he was disabled to an extent, he was very much alive and seemed quite capable of surviving.

As she started thinking about his inevitable departure, she realized how much she had come to love him. When you truly love someone and want what's best for them, you summon up all your strength and wisdom to care for them and then let them go when it's time to let them go. She told him matter-of-factly that it was okay if he wanted to return to where he came from. She did not want him to feel like a prisoner. She said she was happy to help him. He was free to go, if he was ready, if he wanted to.

He was almost ready. He needed to hear more. He needed proof that she had learned what he had come to teach her.

She went on to tell him how much she loved him. She thanked him for taking care of me and her father and her. She looked at his green and grey scaly skin and told him he was beautiful. For the first time she noticed scattered traces of light in hues of crimson, orange, yellow and purple on the newer scales of his skin. His throat was now a vibrant turquoise because when lizards love someone, this is how they show it. He was getting more and more beautiful. Such is the way with love.

She petted his head and his body and his tail and she told him how handsome he was. It was everything he had been waiting to hear. He knew that when someone loves someone this much that they forgive everything. They will not even be aware that forgiveness is needed because they see you as perfect in all that you are and in all that you do. They live their lives in total love for themselves and for you, so that nothing you do can hurt or harm them because their love is stronger than anything that can happen. This level of love wipes every slate clean and becomes the basis of a love that will grow and grow until it is bigger and stronger than anything that could ever threaten to destroy it.

This is the love that Lizard came to teach her. He taught her to love herself by loving him. He taught her to love the same way God loves all of His creatures, for each one is beautiful in His eyes. He taught her to love God more too. He told her that she was his soul mate and that I was too and that God was the father of our soul family. Lizard reminded her that God created us, and God created love. He created everything and He is always the one who is in control. All He wants for us, Lizard told her, is for us to love each other, to love Him and to allow Him to love us.

He knew she would not know for quite some time that he had been teaching her unconditional love all along. He was helping her to bring up all the love inside her heart and to be able to recognize it when it came into her life. He was teaching her to trust. He was teaching her that when you live a life of unconditional love for yourself and for those around you that you can be tuned in on many different levels. You learn to turn the volume of the mind down low enough to be able to hear the voice of the heart. You can clearly see what others cannot see. You live in the power of love.

They both knew that their time together was coming to an end. Life is the school, love is the lesson and she would be completing her studies soon.

Reptiles are among the oldest beings on the planet. I don't know about alligators and crocodiles, but lizards and snakes and many others are very wise old souls. They come back again and again and every time they do they learn more as they advance into higher levels of consciousness.

Lizard said he wasn't sure, but he thought that he probably wouldn't be coming back to earth again. He felt he had reached his highest point and that is why he felt it was now or never to get his message out to others. Hopefully with her good help, he could finally return Home knowing that he had accomplished his goal.

Lizard's destiny seemed to have been fulfilled at last. It was all part of the plan that would come from his needing her care. She could not have learned from him in just an evening. She would not have been able to hear him or his story if she had not learned to be quiet and still and focused on him in each silent moment. Breath by breath, by his very nature, he held her unwavering attention.

She had been completely absorbed by Lizard's needs and he in turn surrounded her with a divine love that would transform her forever.

God is always there but sometimes God can't reach us or touch us. Some people build a wall up against Him. Some of them simply don't believe in Him. Some just forget about Him. What we do to Him we do to ourselves. He is another mirror. He knows this, He designed us this way and this is why He sends unexpected messengers like Lizard. Two-legged, four-legged, feathered or finned, it doesn't matter. They are sent to teach, to give love and to receive love. By doing so they help God to feel the love that has been lost deep inside the soul of the one who forgot about Him.

She finally learned how to take everything at face value without worrying about the What If's. In fact, she learned that worrying about things doesn't help matters at all. What helps the most is the sharing of faith, the use of prayer and loving someone enough to bring out the best in them.

Lizard could have traveled with his injuries to a random house where they would have come after him with broom and dustpan just to throw him in the garbage heap. He traveled, instead, to a place of love and forgiveness. He chose a place that was a safe haven for him. He chose a house of respite, care and kindness. All angels are still learning too and he learned that forgiveness comes easily and he was reminded, once again, that love is more important than anything else.

She learned what she needed to learn and Lizard had learned some things from her too. Once someone learns what a relationship comes to teach, the relationship can move on to make room for new teachers to come in with new lessons and new levels of love.

If a girl can look at a beat-up lizard and think that he is one of the most lovable and beautiful creatures on the planet, what does God see when He looks at her? What do the angels who surround her see when they see her? They see what I saw when I looked at her. They see what she saw when she looked at him. They see through the eyes of love and only love.

If a seemingly ordinary lizard can be worth many days of her time and care, what does God want to do for her? What does He want for all of us? It doesn't matter if we are lizards, sparrows, cats, dogs, people or insects. All living things are loved. We are all cherished and cared for. We all have a purpose. We are all wanted. We are all called Home when our lessons have been learned. We are all in this together.

It was the first of May. She had a deadline to get our book completed. She was doing the final edit at the last minute. The clock was ticking. She was eager to finish. Having spent the better part of two months caregiving Lizard, she was quite surprised that she managed to still be right on track with our book.

That morning she was talking with him on the bench on the front porch. She told him it was May 1 and that it was the day she would be finishing our book. She told him, like she so often had before, that he was free to leave if he wanted to.

Why would today be any different? But it was. There was something different about him. She could see it. She could feel it. She noticed how the sunlight enhanced his scaly reptilian skin, and he was not the usual green and turquoise and purple. He was consumed by the colors of the rainbow. He was glorious. She was overcome with his beauty and touched by the magic that seemed to be him.

It was like a gift that he gave to her, for she brought the love and color with her as she put the finishing touches on our book. Mid-morning she took a break from editing and went out to check on him. Not only was he still surrounded by color, he had actually taken it upon himself to move several inches away from his reliable flat desert rock.

"Well look at you!" she exclaimed in surprise, to the lizard who had never moved of his own accord. He just looked at her. Blinking. Loving.

"I'll be back to see you in just a little while," she said. "I think I'll have Jack's book done by noon. I'll be back to see you as soon as I'm done."

Before she closed the door, she glanced back at him. "I love you Mr. Lizard."

At noon she was finished. She closed up the computer and promptly let out a long, deep sigh to celebrate the intense and long-awaited completion of our book. It had been a labor of love.

After she stood up and stretched, she went over to the front door and opened it, ready to share the good news with our friend. Lizard was nowhere to be found.

She never saw him again.

Lizard was an important spiritual messenger. I don't know if he will return to her. I suppose if she still has similar lessons to learn, she will find him back upon her wall. He came to teach her that every ending is a new beginning. He taught her that she needed to end something before she could start something else. He proved to her that she needed to free herself from the unsettled business of the past before she could move on to a new and promising future.

She doesn't know it yet, but Lizard also taught her how to communicate with the others in our soul family at Rainbow Bridge. He taught her how to connect with me any time she needs me. He taught her to love better than she ever did before. He helped her to recognize love and to be able to communicate from her heart of hearts, the language of everlasting love.

Let Lizard be your teacher too. Don't underestimate anyone who comes into your life. There is always more to life than meets the eye.

Many people think that angels are porcelain-skinned men and women floating above the pastel clouds with white wings, gowns and halos. Angels come in all sizes and shapes. They take all forms. They can be white with white wings, black with white wings, black with black wings. If they want to have rainbow-colored wings they can have rainbow wings, or no wings at all. Once we get to Heaven we can be whatever we want to be.

Some angels are animals; reptiles, birds, fish, insects. Angels can come to earth in any form they wish. They typically put themselves on certain earthly paths where they run into specific animals or people so that they can be in the right place at the right time to teach them and guide them.

Most angels don't just sit around idle, although some do if that's what they want to do. In Heaven we all feel really good and love courses through everything we do and everything we are. When we are lovers, it is not our nature to sit around by ourselves playing a lazy lute or resting on a cloud. When you feel good you want to go out into the big wide world and make a positive difference. You feel love when you feel good and you want to give that love to everyone you meet. As you go along, you find that most others want what you have and they are usually very willing students, wanting to learn what you already learned so long ago.

Heaven, by the way, is not up in the sky somewhere. It is all around us, separated from those on earth by an invisible veil. A veil so thin that sometimes you can't see us, but sometimes you can when conditions are right. If you have faith that angels exist and if your mind is calm and your heart is open, you will see your angels just like we saw Lizard.

Animal Spirits are around you all the time. You don't always see them. At first they will come when you least expect it. They will attract your attention by showing up in unique ways or at unusual times.

Many of us who love you want to be with you. We want to show ourselves to you. Your ordinary life is so busy and consuming that you cannot always see us there. This is why we will come to you in the times when your mind is lazy; the times just before you fall asleep or when you are just waking up. Some of you have learned meditation, which naturally opens the door and pulls back the veil between us.

Animal spirits often will appear during the hours between dusk and dawn; also known as the "tween times." They will always give you something. It may be just a simple pause within the chaos of life to remind you that there is more to life than the details of living it, working it and paying for it. It may be a shred of insight or a flash of recognition that comes to you in a fleeting thought or maybe in a dream in the tween times of your own mind.

Over time you can learn to connect with your special guides and by doing so you will be more connected with your loved ones on both sides of Rainbow Bridge. Sometimes certain loved ones are able to return to you as spirit guides. When you get to know them, you will be able to recognize them by witnessing their personality. We take our personality with us everywhere we go. Just like I learned to recognize Lizard, you will learn to recognize your friends and soul family too. Animal Spirit angels prove to you that there is more to life than meets the eye and much more beyond this life to be discovered.

If a certain animal shows up in your life, ask them what they have to teach you. Don't feel foolish. Look them right in the eye when you talk with them. Listen in your heart for this is where they speak to you.

Study them as you would study an amazing dream, for they come from the same place dreams come from. A place that is more real and more wonderful than the world you think you are living in.

Interpret them, their meaning, their lifestyle and try to see how it fits with your personal life experience. Read up on the unique characteristics of the particular animal who has come into your life. They are your mirror too and they have been chosen specifically for you for a good reason.

The world on earth is just a school. You will have many lessons and many teachers and when you finish your studies you will leave the grand illusion called "life." You will come Home to us and to the great headMaster who sees to it that you always have everything you need to learn to live your life in love.

"Be not forgetful to entertain strangers, for thereby some have entertained angels unawares."
-Hebrews 13:2

ABOUT THE AUTHOR

Kate McGahan has a Master's Degree in Family Mental Health Social Work from Syracuse University and a Bachelor's degree in Social Work from Nazareth College of Rochester.

With over 30 years of experience in hospice and eldercare, Kate has gained a wealth of knowledge based on her work with thousands of individuals and their families. Hired for her expertise, she has found that she also has learned extraordinary lessons from those she has served and come to love.

Life is the school and love is the lesson. Kate will be bringing countless stories to her readers in an entertaining and ultimately thought-provoking way.

It's just the beginning.

Visit Jack on Facebook
http://www.facebook.com/myjackofhearts

Join Jack's Bereavement Support Group
http://www.facebook.com/groups/edgeoftherain
bow

Visit Jack's blog
www.jackmcafghan.com

Subscribe to author updates and get a free book:
www.katemcgahan.com

Printed in Great Britain
by Amazon

RE-EXAMINING
SUCCESS

Raising pupils'
examination
performance at
secondary school:
systems, techniques,
processes and
partners

RE-EXAMINING
SUCCESS

Raising pupils'
examination
performance at
secondary school:
systems, techniques,
processes and
partners

David W Hughes

The author has made every effort to ensure the accuracy of information contained in this publication, but assumes no responsibility for any errors, inaccuracies, inconsistencies and omissions. Likewise, every effort has been made to contact copyright holders. If any copyright material has been reproduced unwittingly and without permission the publisher will gladly receive information enabling them to rectify any error or omission in subsequent editions.

British Library Cataloguing in Publication Data
A CIP record for this book is available from the British Library

ISBN: 978-1-913063-09-2

This book is also available in the following e-book formats:
MOBI ISBN: 978-1-913063-10-8
EPUB ISBN: 978-1-913063-11-5
Adobe e-book ISBN: 978-1-913063-12-2

Cartoon illustrations by Élisabeth Eudes-Pascal represented by GCI

Cover and text design by Out of House Limited
Project Management by Newgen Publishing UK
Print managed and manufactured by Jellyfish Solutions

Critical Publishing
3 Connaught Road
St Albans
AL3 5RX

www.criticalpublishing.com

FSC

CONTENTS

CONTENTS

You cannot teach a man anything;
you can only help him find it within himself.

Galileo Galilei (1564–1642)
Italian physicist and astronomer

MEET THE AUTHOR

DAVID W HUGHES

I have taught and led within the secondary and tertiary sectors for over 30 years, working in successful and failing schools. I have led improvement projects at local, regional and national levels. I have served on the Children's Society Commission for education in Birmingham and I support schools and universities in development programmes. While working on the Building Schools for the Future programme, I was seconded for almost two years to support the development of the Opening Minds curriculum, devised in collaboration with the Confederation of British Industry as a twenty-first-century learning model for schools, which mirrored the world's most effective educational systems and addressed the attitudes, behaviours and competences required of the modern learner. I am an associate of the University of Nottingham School of Education and a writer for the educational press.

I post regularly on my blog: https://learningrenaissance.wordpress.com/

This is a resource focused on the future of learning at a time that could well be termed the Renaissance in Learning. The aim is to share innovative practice and resources to help create a climate in which every learner can succeed.

ACKNOWLEDGEMENTS

The publisher and author would like to express their grateful thanks to the following people and organisations for use of copyright material.

Professor Amanda Kirby for the use of Figure 14.2 on quality of life impact.
Kevin Hewitson for the use of the learning quotient infographic in Figure 13.2.
Microsoft Corporation for permission to use screenshots in Figures 11.1, 11.2 and 11.3.
Plasq.com for permission to use the screenshot from their Comic Life, Figure 11.4.
Ross Morrison McGill of Teacher Toolkit, for inspiring Table 4.1, initiative bingo.
The RSA Opening Minds Curriculum and the RSA Academy for recollections of the lesson
   structure in Table 8.1.

The author would also like to thank the following schools in which he was lucky enough to serve with some wonderful, committed and forward-thinking staff.

Swavesey Village College, Cambridgeshire, in particular David Rooney, who gave me my first job
   in teaching, and Sheila Ginn who was a professional mentor to me in the first stages of my
   career.
Hartford High School, Cheshire.
Alderman Derbyshire School, Nottinghamshire.
Dukeries College, Nottinghamshire.
RSA Academy, Sandwell, in particular Mick Gernon, the Founding Principal.

Author dedication

I would like to pay particular tribute to my wife Jane, who took my febrile notes and turned them into short sentences with appropriate grammar and punctuation for publication. This is the second time she has endured this process in my support.

To Luke and Lucy, Owen and Dalia for being so enthusiastic, and finally to Iolo the Labrador for showing formidable impulse control when my writing ate into his walking time.

To Julia and Di at Critical Publishing for their unfailing support and enthusiasm, without which the book would not have come to fruition.

INTRODUCTION

Motivation and purpose

My primary motivation for writing this book is as an act of pupil advocacy. The examination process is a particularly harsh ordeal to impose on a person of any age. But, for young people in secondary schools, it tests their emotional resilience at a time of a tsunami of changes in their lives. I characterise the interests, motivations and progress of the learner as the micro-level of analysis within the book.

My secondary motivation is to challenge teaching colleagues to look more fundamentally at the process of preparing all pupils for examinations. This is the macro-level of analysis. Specifically, I have three concerns.

1. To explore the relationship between the learning regime across the two years of a GCSE level or Advanced level syllabus and the 'revision period' to see if expectations, processes and activities are congruent from the point of view of the pupil.

2. To come to a belated realisation that approaches to examination preparation, if they are to be successful, need to be personalised to the needs of the individual learner. If they are not, and every pupil has the same diet in a revision programme, you disenfranchise the most vulnerable and insecure learners to underachieve in the examinations, with related damage to their subsequent learning mindset and life chances.

3. For pupils to achieve to their full potential, schools cannot grant study leave without ensuring they have addressed parents' concerns. Parents want to support their children to make the most of this independent study period so they arrive at the examinations calm, well-prepared and positive they can overcome the examination challenge.

These three considerations underlie a more fundamental concern that teachers need to address, namely what constitutes success in the examinations for individual pupils. This is where the micro elements that drive the individual pupil overlap with the macro-level of whole-school concerns.

Within the 30-year span of my teaching career, the orthodoxy was that the purpose of the school was to maximise the examination success of every pupil. This, after all, was the foremost arbiter of the success of the school. Indeed, as an institution, it would be difficult for a school to focus on any other statement of intent. Parents wanted this, pupils wanted this, the state wanted this, PISA international education comparisons emphasised this and senior leadership teams, the governors, and Ofsted were charged with ensuring that this was the case in every school.

This focus on school responsibility and accountability, which was both laudable and necessary to enhance pupils' life chances, did have a considerable downside. This was the emphasis on more efficient ways to deliver curriculum content, rather than with broader concerns about the effectiveness of the learning received and implemented by the individual pupil.

Why I am qualified to write this book

My teaching experience has been confined to the English education system. However, my career has spanned experiences in a very wide range of schools, in part due to secondments and project management experience at local authority and national levels. This led to my work with leadership teams and individual teachers on learning transformation projects and cultural changes in learning models.

I have also visited schools in other countries to explore how they address their macro-level drivers and the experiences of pupils at the micro-level.

In the past decade, social media and technological developments have enabled me to collaborate with, and learn from, the experience of teachers and learners worldwide. I have helped to develop online courses for master's degrees in Educational Leadership and have mentored trainee teachers across the globe. Conversations with teachers from five continents indicate that the concerns regarding revision strategies and the relationship between revision and more general learning outlined in this book represent a universal concern.

A great source of inspiration for me has been the input of former pupils going back to the start of my teaching career. I have been honoured by invitations to a number of student reunions and, since I finished full-time school teaching, social media has put me in contact with many more former pupils, some of whom are now middle-aged. I am always interested in their experiences after school and how happy and fulfilled they are. They are always keen to remind me of memories of incidents and experiences in my classes or on residentials.

What strikes me about their anecdotes is that not one recounts a factual thing I taught them. Every anecdote focuses on not the *what* but the *how* of learning. I find this particularly gratifying as I have, since my own school days, had an interest in what, at the time, could be encompassed by the term 'study skills'. This has now expanded to include a whole plethora of elements comprising emotional and physical resilience and well-being, metacognition and independent learning.

My teacher training at the University of York was in a department that contained the Centre for the Study of the Comprehensive School and was devoted to leading research on effective learning. I was committed to a learning approach that emphasised a holistic idea of the *how* of learning, rather than being committed to subject knowledge per se. I had completed a multidisciplinary degree, and found in York's Education Department a commitment to integrated courses in which pupil initiative, independent learning and interpretive skills were promoted.

I determined to teach and lead humanities departments comprising English, history, geography and religious education. I always held a more rounded view of learning than colleagues in single-subject departments. Where they emphasised the uniqueness of their subject content and methodology, I looked to develop a series of learning strategies that emphasised the unity of approaches to learning and teaching.

Seeing the child as an individual and being cognisant of particular circumstances

We are in the midst of what some commentators consider to be a 'mental health crisis' in secondary schools. The purported reasons for this are many and various, most lying outside the remit of education, but nonetheless impacting on it. In preparing pupils for the national statutory examinations, schools need to ensure that they are doing all in their power to support the health and mental well-being of their pupils. This requires that schools are proactive in supporting pupils through the full examination period in a way that few schools are currently addressing.

Child mental health and well-being were to be a short postscript to the book but, in the course of researching, two disturbing reports were published about child mental health. The first was compiled by NHS Digital (2019) and the second by the OECD (2018). The first focused on the UK, while the second was concerned with the whole of Europe. They came to some strikingly similar conclusions, which many have chosen to describe as a child mental health crisis in their scale and intensity.

Although a wide range of behavioural and emotional conditions were reported to have sharply increased in incidence across childhood, there were particularly high spikes of depression and anxiety associated with the ages 13 to 18. Coupled to the natural growth and hormonal changes that accompany the teenage years, it is clear that emotional and mental health are most in jeopardy across the teenage population precisely at the time of the national examinations.

I consider this new information warrants a chapter in the book devoted to addressing the issues of child mental health related to the examinations.

Even if we set aside the mental health and well-being elements of young people, the examinations do not constitute the 'level playing field' they purport to be. The examinations, particularly in their 'study leave' element, make massive assumptions about the ability of pupils to respond effectively to a period of independent, autonomous and self-regulated study.

A comfortable and quiet room, books and materials, access to the internet and regular food and drink might be considered as basic requirements, but even these are beyond the reach of a large and ever-increasing group of pupils growing up in poverty.

Coupled to those in care, those in hospital and other socially vulnerable families, the egalitarian and fair premise on which the examination system is based erodes quickly. The standard examination becomes deeply weighted towards those pupils in relatively prosperous households, with robust support systems from the family and every opportunity to be successful in the ordeal of the examinations.

Government statistics for the UK published in 2019 indicate that 3.5 million children (26 per cent) (Francis-Devine et al, 2019) live in absolute low income. This trend is continuing to grow, mostly due to the working poor having incomes that are shrinking relatively. That represents one in four children in schools generally, and significantly more than that in the poorest wards in the country.

The book intends to address these issues and suggest some ways in which every pupil can thrive in their general learning, and develop the independent and autonomous learning skills necessary to thrive in the examination system and in life beyond school.

Threats and opportunities

From the above, it might be considered that I am arguing against the format of the current examination system per se. I would deploy that argument if I thought it had even the remotest chance of being successful. However, that argument must wait for riper times of change. In the meantime, we must deal with the reality of the examinations as they currently exist and seek to ameliorate their worst aspects and prepare young people far better to survive them and thrive.

Nevertheless, this book is written at an interesting and potentially more receptive time for its message. The direction of travel in English education (although I sense parallels from conversations with colleagues in American, Australian and Indian schools) has been to enshrine the public examination as a gold standard of assessment.

Under a previous British Education Secretary, notorious for believing that he had heard more than enough of the words of experts, the return to formal written examinations and the abandonment of coursework was a necessary requirement of a 'rigorous system' (Mance, 2016; Meikle, 2012).

This was despite the fact that coursework was a broader examination of the skills of an individual pupil, requiring individual research, hypothesis testing and presentations skills to be deployed. This argument was couched in terms of a lack of rigour in the assessment of coursework components and concerns about performance inflation by teachers on behalf of their pupils. The corollary was that the examination provided an unimpeachable 'level playing field' that was beyond the ability of individual teachers to influence.

Move forward a few years and now we have concerns that the ruling orthodoxy in government dogma of schools being held accountable for producing exponential and continual improvements in pupil outcomes is producing 'examination factories'. This ethos is producing the collateral damage of the mental well-being of pupils and staff. Mental health is sacrificed to the short-term good of maximising examination achievement.

The summer of 2018 has seen reported evidence of the widespread use of 'off-rolling' of pupils out of A level courses if their projected performance undermines the global achievement figures of the educational establishment. There have been reports of grade deflation and inflation in key stage testing so that schools can maximise the added value that they confer on the educational attainment of their pupils.

Her Majesty's Chief Inspector of Education, Children's Services and Skills, Amanda Spielman, has commented negatively on the 'examination factory' mentality of many schools and the toll it is taking on the mental well-being of pupils, as well as issues related to the recruitment and retention of staff (Adams, 2018).

So perhaps more radical, fundamental change is coming, at a cultural and national level, which will provide pupils with a more rational and equitable pathway to access their future goals.

Structure of the book

Given the points regarding school structures and cultures, pupils' learning and motivation techniques, and parental involvement and support of learning, the book is divided into these three elements.

Each element gives the school leader and teacher access to research and observations that support a review and regeneration of how they prepare pupils for formal examinations.

As a minimum, it is hoped that the book will provoke a review of the revision practices provided for supporting pupils in examinations.

I would hope that schools would make more profound use of the book to support a cultural review of how they teach, how they prepare pupils and engage parents in a holistic programme of support prior to and during examinations.

Such a comprehensive programme enables all pupils to truly maximise their potential and have meaningful choices as to how to continue their education beyond statutory age in further or higher education.

That the examination techniques introduced here can help to give pupils a growth mindset and a structured and fearless attitude to examinations is all the better, for such an attitude is the basis of the successful independent and autonomous lifelong learner, on whom the future prosperity of the country depends.

Within the book, triangulation points are used as pauses in the narrative to enable readers to reflect on the chapter content and compare it to their own circumstances and experiences. These may also contain prompts to help develop new understanding into individual and school research avenues or technique development.

My personal experiences in change management in engagement with pupils, teachers, senior leaders, governors and parents are recounted in 'Case studies'. These ensure that I ground any theoretical analysis with practical implementation examples.

Each chapter has a reading list to enable further research, with particularly significant texts highlighted and explored in more detail.

Bibliography

Adams, R (2018) Ofsted Inspectors to Stop Using Exam Results as Key Mark of Success. *Guardian*. [online] Available at: www.theguardian.com/education/2018/oct/11/ofsted-to-ditch-using-exam-results-as-mark-of-success-amanda-spielman (accessed 19 September 2019).

Francis-Devine, B, Booth, L and McGuiness, F (2019) Poverty in the UK: Statistics. [online] Available at: https://researchbriefings.files.parliament.uk/documents/SN07096/SN07096.pdf (Accessed 19 September 2019).

Mance, H (2016) Britain Has Had Enough of Experts, Says Gove. *Financial Times*. [online] Available at: www.ft.com/content/3be49734-29cb-11e6-83e4-abc22d5d108c (accessed 11 September 2019).

Meikle, J (2012) GCSEs Are Dead: The EBacc is the Future, Says Michael Gove. *Guardian*. [online] Available at: www.theguardian.com/education/2012/sep/17/gcse-ebacc-michael-gove (accessed 11 September 2019).

NHS Digital (2019) National Study of Health and Wellbeing: Children and Young People. [online] Available at: https://digital.nhs.uk/data-and-information/areas-of-interest/public-health/national-study-of-health-and-wellbeing-children-and-young-people (accessed 11 September 2019).

OECD (2018) *Children & Young People's Mental Health in the Digital Age: Shaping the Future*. Geneva: Organisation for Economic Co-operation and Development. [online] Available at: www.oecd.org/els/health-systems/Children-and-Young-People-Mental-Health-in-the-Digital-Age.pdf (accessed 19 September 2019).

Section A

BUILDING A WHOLE-SCHOOL PROGRAMME FOR LEARNING TRANSFORMATION

This book is organised into two sections. Section A explores what amounts to a mandate for progressive change in the way education works. It is based on recognising the redundancy of much that we take for granted in the priorities, structures and practices in current schools.

From term times to lessons, content to delivery, from teacher exposition to the examination system, much of the daily work of schools is extremely wasteful of the talents of the young people for whom access to learning represents their preparation for a changing future.

We have seen in the crises of teacher recruitment and retention that it is equally corrosive to the mental and physical health and well-being of those charged with delivering the existing model of learning.

We are, in effect, trying to impose an increasingly dysfunctional, historical model of learning onto a rapidly changing future. We seem to be in thrall to those, many of whom are politicians, who believe that the best way to address the future is to double down on existing practices and structures.

This book is a call to arms for teachers – to you! For you to have confidence in your professional expertise and determination to learn from others and so improve the lot of all pupils; to equip pupils to survive and thrive in the challenges and opportunities the future will hold for them.

Section A provides insights for educational leaders to explore more comprehensively the range and scope of changes needed to revitalise and repurpose educational provision in their own schools. The section proceeds from a survey of the wider educational drivers and processes at the national level down to the analysis of teaching and learning priorities and strategies. International comparisons are introduced to show the direction of learning in countries that have a more rational and intimate view of the patterns and requirements needed to shape future provision.

For the sceptics, or the complacent, a case study is provided at the end of the section in Chapter 8, showing how the most fundamental realignment of education and learning was conceived and delivered in an English school.

1. THE EXAMINATIONS PROCESS: ANTECEDENTS. ANOMALIES AND LIMITATIONS IN THE TWENTY-FIRST CENTURY

Critical issues

» Limitations of the format of the examinations system in developing learners.

» Limitations of the equality of opportunity of the current examinations system.

» Limitations of the scope of the examinations system in providing 'job ready' lifelong learners.

» Limited attempts at reform of the current examinations system.

» New directions in learning: the growing distance between current examinations and the effective twenty-first-century learner.

Limitations of the format of the examination system

The public examinations process, as internationally constituted, is the most eminently fair and equitable system designed to test pupils in national examinations at statutory levels. It gives every pupil the same circumstances, time constraints and environmental conditions in which to respond to the standard questions. If the school invigilation teams are doing their job and ensuring there are no infringements of the rules, then every pupil has an equal opportunity to demonstrate their ability. This is incontrovertible.

Put another way, over the whole programme of study of perhaps two years in which the pupil has prepared for the examination, the last one to three hours in which they are tested is the only point that can be guaranteed to be equitable.

Up until entry into the examination room, myriad other factors are in play:

- access to good teaching;
- home support;
- access to online resources;
- places to study outside school;
- access to books;
- support from peers and mentors;
- access to professional tutors;
- freedom from illness to enable pupils to attend school;
- an adequate diet;
- sufficient sleep;
- access to role models/aspirational role models;
- parents in work;
- freedom from poverty.

All these factors make the examination less a test of the native ability and aptitude of the pupil, and more a trial of circumstances beyond the control of the individual pupil. I am not arguing here that pupils with more difficult circumstances cannot do well in examinations. I am arguing that such pupils succeed despite the system, not because it efficiently and effectively recognises their educational potential at the point of statutory testing (Gillett, 2017).

I am passionate about the efficacy of the examination system from personal experience. I grew up on a council estate and thoroughly enjoyed it. It was a marvellous community with exceptional role models in fairness, family orientation and entrepreneurship. Nonetheless, it offered few examples of formal educational success. My passage to university was supported materially by my parents (who had lost the pathway to further and higher education to the Great Depression and the Second World War), an uncle who was a Labour councillor and an aunt who was a staff manager at a popular high street department store. Their ability to see beyond tomorrow and invest in the future through study today was what gave me an opportunity to succeed in what would otherwise have been an educational lottery. Many children far more talented than me did not get this opportunity to thrive in study. Many succeeded through other pathways but too much native talent was wasted for want of sufficient support at critical times in their schooling.

Limitations of the equality of opportunity of the examinations system

If I suggested that you wilfully neglect a section of the cohort of pupils entering both their GCSEs and A levels as an experiment in social engineering, you would be aghast. If I suggested that you leave the top performing 20 per cent of your pupils to their own devices and concentrated all your efforts on the remaining 80 per cent with a disproportionate bias to those with the greatest social disadvantage, how would you react? Would your parents or governors support this policy?

This would be seen as a preposterous position to take and would fly in the face of all your school stood for: excellence, opportunity and hard work.

Now let us reverse the proposition and suggest you abandon the bottom 20 per cent of your pupil cohort to their own devices and whatever support they could muster.

Again, this is a preposterous proposition which makes a mockery of your school's proud position of equal opportunity and support for all. But would there be such an outrage from parents and governors?

I am suggesting that this is what is, in fact, happening because of the assumptions schools make about the capacity of pupils from less advantaged backgrounds to develop the self-supported study skills that underpin academic success.

Limitations of the scope of the examinations system

There is an element used to justify all intense ordeals, from the long hours incurred as a junior doctor to military service that highlights the mindset 'Well, I went through it, and it didn't do me any harm!' This, of course, is always said by those who survived the ordeal intact and with limited emotional or psychological damage. That, of course, ignores two critical aspects.

1. Such testing regimes are faced by adults with greater maturity and experience. This is not a justification of the process, merely recognition that, hopefully, the person undergoing the process has developed the maturity to survive the ordeal. The burnout rate of junior doctors, military veterans suffering from PTSD and, for that matter, young teachers in schools, should lead us to different conclusions about the efficacy of these processes.

2. Military training and the experience of being a junior doctor or young teacher are transitory processes. There is a better time beyond the difficulties. For young people in the secondary school examinations process, the motivational factor, implicit or explicit, is that their whole future life experiences are entwined with their ability to thrive in a series of formal written examinations. This is both only partially true and fundamentally unhelpful in motivating them.

Compounding the problem of public examinations in secondary school is the issue of study leave. For five years, pupils are presented with a model of pedagogy in which the teacher teaches and the pupils listen and make notes and complete simulation exercises with support. Within weeks of the most critical tests of their young careers, they are ejected from school for 'study leave', and expected to work with a completely different learning model.

Effective study leave requires that the pupil instantaneously adopts a model based on working independently and autonomously with only the collected pearls of wisdom of the various subject departments to guide them on a programme of revision. Little wonder that so many pupils underperform. Worse, the most vulnerable pupils face the greatest challenges.

Pupils in care, outside the formal school system through exclusion, in hospital, with learning disabilities or in poverty do not conform to the expectations many schools have in their revision programmes. For them, there may not be a secure home, supportive adults, a wholesome diet or even a space of quiet and calm in which to study.

The die-hards will argue that the written examination is the time-honoured method of terminal assessment adopted by the great universities. It is not.

The great universities, going back to medieval times and before, from Padua to Alexandria, from Oxford and Cambridge to Heidelberg and Leuven, never used formal written examinations. Their assessment methodology was the viva voce, the oral examination in which the 'mettle of the man' (man because women in formal education in the higher education world only began to occur selectively from the late nineteenth century onwards) could be tested and the moral and ethical standards of the person gleaned from the quality of their reasoning and underlying assumptions.

The formal written examination is a format that only emerged with the rapid expansion of education at all levels in the nineteenth century, when the state made the connection between economic well-being and education, and particularly with literacy and numeracy levels being critical to economic success.

Moreover, the formal written examination is not a measure of excellence because its remit is so constrained. It looks only at the ability to recall information in a written format and under a time constraint. Little wonder that those in industry and commerce comment with disbelief that after all the years of formal education, young people arrive in their first period of employment so poorly prepared for the challenges and opportunities of work; indeed young people believe it themselves (Kashefpakdel, 2017; CBI, 2018).

UNIVERSAL EDUCATION PROVISION WITH A TRIPARTITE ELEMENT

The search for a more rational and expansive curriculum that would prove more challenging and stimulating for pupils and would give them greater insights into life and employment beyond school has a long and convoluted history in the UK.

The 1944 Education Act sought to ensure that every child received a secondary education and also promoted a tripartite system of schools. This tripartite division recognised that, broadly speaking, jobs came in three different categories:

1. managerial and professional jobs, which required further educational qualifications beyond statutory education;

2. clerical and administrative jobs, which required a foundation of a particular skill set that could be started in formal education and continued after school in 'on the job' and apprenticeship training;

3. trade jobs, for which the foundations, in the form of woodwork, metalwork and car maintenance, could be developed in school and honed further in an apprenticeship beyond school.

These three elements were reflected in the three types of schools:

1. grammar schools for those destined for managerial and professional careers;

2. secondary moderns for those who would fill the clerical and administrative roles;

3. technical schools for those being prepared for trade apprenticeships.

There was much to commend this system in providing a broad range of curricula that were appropriate to future roles. Whereas the grammar schools maintained the criteria of the formal examination, the testing in the two other school formats was much broader. Secondary moderns and technical schools required the individual pupil to work for extended periods on projects of a practical nature such as sample documents, model cakes and pastries, wooden or metal project pieces. Pupils needed to demonstrate a wide range of construction techniques or the ability to be observed stripping, repairing and reassembling a component of a motor car (Education Act, 1944; Trueman, 2015).

Some schools went further in promoting skills with an eye to the local economy. A school in the Nottinghamshire coalfield actually constructed, with the aid of the National Coal Board, a mock coal face in its grounds so that pupils could acclimatise themselves to the rigours of working underground in their future career. They also attended some of their lessons at the local colliery. This innovation was vividly captured in a film held in the Pathé News Archives in 1947 (British Pathé, 1947).

This breadth of educational experience in the secondary school phase, innovative as it was, did not come without issues. First, the whole system was based on the rather bizarre concept that the abilities of the child were set and largely immutable by the age of 11 and that a simple, formal examination called the '11-Plus' could effectively group pupils into the three schooling types.

The main proponent of this system was Sir Cyril Burt, a psychologist. He believed that educational ability was usually inherited by children and that this ability could be proven in an examination taken at the end of primary school. The test really rewarded reading, writing and language, and mathematical comprehension skills. Important as they are, these skill sets alone cannot be said to comprise academic ability.

Put charitably, it may be said that the experimental methods by which Burt had come to these conclusions about ability had a number of statistical anomalies. Put less charitably, he manipulated the results to confirm his preferred model. Such revelations were part of the reason that the comprehensive system, which abandoned the discredited 11-Plus examination, gathered such momentum in the 1960s.

Second, the spurious nature of the 11-Plus could be gleaned from the fact that each year it was able to sort the pupils into the exact proportion of provision that each of the three types of schools offered in the local area. It was, therefore, not a rational test of ability but a rather brutal rationing mechanism.

Third, there was not parity of esteem between the three educational pathways at secondary level. Grammar school was the destination of choice for children of all aspirational parents, but was usually limited to no more than 20 per cent of the school population. In this rationing system, parents who had themselves sat the 11-Plus or the matriculation examination that had preceded it were best prepared and most highly motivated to ensure their children received the best preparation at home and school to succeed in the examination. This also explains why the 11-Plus and the grammar school system still persist in some areas in the UK: because those in managerial positions of responsibility and therefore able to reform it are those most likely to have benefited from the system. They also have the support of all those parents who have similarly benefited, and a surprising number of aspirant parents who will support such brutal rationing of educational opportunity in the belief that their child will succeed in the test at age 11.

In such areas, the whole system is geared to providing for those 20 per cent of pupils that the spurious 11-Plus examination deems worthy of a grammar school place. By default, those who do not secure such a place are deemed to have failed in their learning at age 11.

This failure is based on the arbitrary nature of an examination heavily weighted towards those pupils coming from a secure family background: pupils whose parents benefited from this same system, with access to books and, if necessary, access to private tutors. If the 11-Plus examination was so precise a tool at identifying ability then it would spell the end of the lucrative private tutor industry in this country!

At this point, educationalists usually compare the British system, with its inherent faults, to that of Germany. There, for many years, the different educational pathways have been characterised by parity of esteem, in which academic and vocational prowess are valued equally.

Despite this obsession with the current examination system as the 'gold standard' in our education system, there are attempts in play to devise a broader, more rational and inclusive educational system.

Limited attempts at reform of the examinations system

One development strand is championed by the author of the original 1988 Education Act, which did much to define the landscape of British education.

Lord Baker, or Kenneth Baker as he was in the 1980s, recognised that the national curriculum, as it developed, did not address the needs of British industry to provide sufficient pupils with technical and vocational skills at all academic levels. The result was a dire shortage of apprentices, and technical and managerial staff with a scientific background. This threatened the ability to innovate, design and manage the technical projects that the UK had traditionally excelled at on the world stage.

Such shortcomings would hamper future national prosperity, so needed to be addressed urgently. Current estimates still suggest that the UK needs some 200,000 level 3 and above (A level and degree level) engineers and technical workers and that, in particular, the failure to attract females to the sector represents a lamentable waste of talent and resources (Education Act, 1988).

The antidote to this problem that Lord Baker proposed was the University Technical College (University Technical Colleges, 2010) approach. In this, a new tier of technically biased schools were set up in the 14–19 sector to address the need for more technically competent pupils at both apprenticeship and graduate levels. The use of the term UTC was a clever portmanteau, designed to capture the interest of aspirational parents and young people. In an age of uncertain employment, there was a suggestion that pupils were being trained for an area of the economy with defined and persistent employment opportunities (Engineering UK, 2018).

Many employers – such as the heavy plant manufacturer JCB, aerospace manufacturer BAE Systems, Rolls Royce, Siemens, the Royal Navy and numerous others – quickly endorsed the programme with sponsorship deals, as did local universities.

The UTC system has bridged the gap between school and employment with more innovative learning programmes that stress the technical and scientific challenges and key skills underpinning an effective education for the twenty-first century. Teamwork, research, problem-solving and presentation skills are all emphasised. The involvement of large employers and universities means that pupils have the opportunity to deploy their new found skills in real-time problem-solving, often in industrial settings and with real kit, rather than through classroom-based simulations from textbooks. To some extent, this could form part of the template of a future education which decouples the learning experience of pupils from classroom activity and gives opportunities to develop broad-based and relevant skills for the changing world of work beyond formal education (University Technical Colleges, 2019).

Despite these positive attributes, there are limitations to the UTC programme. The UTCs offer a 14–19 education, so that pupils have experienced a secondary school education before having to opt to leave their existing school to join a UTC. This means UTCs represent a discontinuity with the existing educational structure (Burke, 2018).

It is a brave, well informed and innovative parent who will make the leap of faith to withdraw their child from their existing school to trust the UTC to take them through formal examinations – with the expectation that they will continue in school-based education through to the age of 19. Even the underlying assumption that they will be more valuable to local engineering, scientific or technical employers, and therefore have job opportunities built into the system, has not proved sufficient enticement to support the growth of UTCs. There have been notable and high-profile failures of UTCs, which have dented confidence in the programme, and the future of UTCs is now in jeopardy (Burke, 2017; Adams, 2018).

Towards the curriculum of the future

The preceding analysis has demonstrated the limitations in trying to reform the present UK curriculum to produce a fairer, more rigorous and more effective preparation for all young people to face the challenges and opportunities of the twenty-first century. There is no longer uniform education provision in the home countries, as Northern Ireland, Scotland and Wales have legislatures that have devolved responsibility for educational provision. Subsequently, my comments are increasingly confined to experience in England. Traditionally, the starting point for review has been the limitations of the current system, so that the need for A levels is demanded by the university sector. While decrying the poor literacy and numeracy output of schools, many employers fall back on demanding more mathematics and English content in schools. The government takes as its terms of reference for change, the existing subject curriculum and the knowledge base that underpins it.

Taken together, this means that those with an interest in changing outcomes are wedded to existing delivery methods and those with the power to change things only contemplate marginal amendments to the existing structures of knowledge and delivery. Meanwhile, pupils are short-changed and prevented from experiencing a range of appropriate and challenging learning experiences to prepare them for lifelong learning in the twenty-first century.

As I write, Ofsted, the gatekeeper of educational standards, has announced a curriculum review. The narrow remit and recruitment of expertise wedded to maintaining the existing delivery system will ensure that little of portent will change following the review. Therefore, we shall fall further behind both in international competitiveness and in the life chances available to our young people (Hazell, 2019).

Meanwhile, those countries above us on the Organisation for Economic Co-operation and Development (OECD) table of educational performance are undertaking root and branch reviews. In Singapore, this means the abandonment of the traditional examination as the arbiter of the effectiveness of the educational system. Ong Ye Kung, Singapore's Education Minister, stated, 'Learning is not a competition.' The Ministry of Education is planning a series of changes aimed at discouraging comparisons between student performance and encouraging individuals to concentrate on their own learning development (World Economic Forum, 2018).

Meanwhile, colleagues in Finland confirm that the country has accepted the limitations of a curriculum defined by knowledge demonstrated in a traditional examination system and indeed of knowledge as the vital currency of learning. They are moving towards extended project-based learning in which the pupil has greater responsibility and autonomy for their learning and skills development. The teacher will move from a whole-class teaching role to one of personalised mentor to pupils negotiating their way through their extended skills-based research projects (Spiller, 2017). Additionally they have abandoned examinations and a quality control system based on a rigorous inspection regime (Alexander and Orange, 2013).

❖ Triangulation point

For your own school, consider how well the current examination system has served your pupils.

1. **Do you compile destination data of all the pupils leaving your school? What do these figures tell you about how well you have matched your pupils to employment opportunities?**

2. **What are the most and least effective elements of your careers and guidance provision?**

3. **How effective is your provision in terms of having employers providing curriculum challenges in your school?**

4. **How effective is your liaison work with local colleges of education offering vocational pathways?**

Summary

We have seen that the role of the examination has been central to the path of educational development and that it has effectively acted as a rationing system for educational progression. The case has been made that the examinations system is deeply flawed in both the narrowness of the skills tested and the inflation of the claims that it represents an effective arbiter of pupil ability. That the examination is based on dubious research data has long been known, with the discrediting of the originator of the 11-Plus examination, Cyril Burt (Khyade, 2016).

But the damaging legacy of Burt's spurious conclusions still proves to be popular. This is because it rewards those with most to gain from the educational rationing represented by a selective grammar school system. It gives children from such backgrounds greater access to higher education. There is little appetite for change among those who benefit from the existing system. In the meantime, the relationship between examination performance and Ofsted gradings has led to schools cynically 'off-rolling' pupils who they consider will not make a positive contribution (Robertson, 2018).

Clearly, although a wholesale review and update of the examination system to reflect the effective lifelong learner of the twenty-first century is some time away, it will happen. The limitations of English, if not UK, examination practice will be thrown into sharp relief as our international competitiveness is constrained and others take a more progressive attitude to developing the capacity of all their learners.

Bibliography

Adams, R (2018) Half of University Technical College Students Drop Out, Report Finds. *Guardian*. [online] Available at: www.theguardian.com/education/2018/oct/11/university-technical-colleges-schools-report-education-policy-institute (accessed 11 September 2019).

Alexander, H and Orange, R (2013) OECD Education Report: Finland's No Inspections, No League Tables and Few Exams Approach. [online] Available at: www.telegraph.co.uk/news/worldnews/europe/finland/10489070/OECD-education-report-Finlands-no-inspections-no-league-tables-and-few-exams-approach.html (accessed 11 September 2019).

British Pathé (1947) Mining School 1947. [online] Available at: www.britishpathe.com/video/mining-school/query/centre (accessed 11 September 2019).

Burke, J (2017) Gove Admits the UTCs Experiment Has Failed. *FE Week*. [online] Available at: https://feweek.co.uk/2017/02/10/gove-admits-the-utcs-experiment-has-failed/ (accessed 11 September 2019).

Burke, J (2018) Revealed: Low Pupil Numbers Forced Nearly Every UTC to Hand Funding Back. *Schools Week*. [online] Available at: https://schoolsweek.co.uk/revealed-low-pupil-numbers-forced-nearly-every-utc-to-hand-funding-back/ (accessed 11 September 2019).

CBI (2018) Half of Young People Do Not Feel Prepared for World of Work: CBI/Accenture/Hays Survey. [online] Available at: www.cbi.org.uk/media-centre/articles/half-of-young-people-do-not-feel-prepared-for-world-of-work-cbi-accenture-hays-survey/ (accessed 11 September 2019).

Education Act (1944) [online] Available at: www.legislation.gov.uk/ukpga/Geo6/7-8/31/contents/enacted (accessed 11 September 2019).

Education Act (1988) [online] Available at: www.legislation.gov.uk/ukpga/1988/40/contents (accessed 11 September 2019).

Engineering UK (2018) Engineering UK 2018: Synopsis and Recommendations. [online] Available at: www.engineeringuk.com/media/1576/7444_enguk18_synopsis_standalone_aw.pdf (accessed 11 September 2019).

Gillett, R (2017) Science Says Parents of Successful Kids Have 17 Things in Common. *Business Insider*. [online] Available at: www.businessinsider.com/how-to-raise-successful-kids-2017-3?r=UK#-1 (accessed 11 September 2019).

Hazell, W (2019) Ofsted Accused of 'Pedagogical Bias' Over Subject Advisers for New Inspections. *TES*. [online] Available at: www.tes.com/news/ofsted-accused-pedagogical-bias-over-subject-advisers-new-inspections (accessed 11 September 2019).

Kashefpakdel, E (2017) How Work-Ready Are Your Students? *SecEd*. [online] Available at: www.sec-ed.co.uk/news/how-work-ready-are-your-students/ (accessed 11 September 2019).

Khyade, V B (2016) In the Memory of Sir Cyril Lodowic Burt. *International Academic Journal of Humanities*, 3(9): 15–21. [online] Available at: http://iaiest.com/dl/journals/4-%20IAJ%20of%20Humanities/v3-i9-sep2016/paper2.pdf (accessed 11 September 2019).

Robertson, A (2018) Spielman Warns that Off-rolling 'Could Get Worse' After Sharp Rise in Pupils Leaving Schools before GCSEs. *Schools Week*. [online] Available at: https://schoolsweek.co.uk/spielman-off-rolling-could-get-worse-after-sharp-rise-in-pupils-leaving-school-before-gcses/ (accessed 11 September 2019).

Spiller, P (2017) Could Subjects Soon Be a Thing of the Past in Finland? *BBC News*. [online] Available at: www.bbc.co.uk/news/world-europe-39889523 (accessed 11 September 2019).

Trueman, C N (2015) Tripartitie Education. *History Learning Site*. [online] Available at: www.historylearningsite.co.uk/sociology/education-and-sociology/tripartitie-education/ (accessed 11 September 2019).

University Technical Colleges (2010) Initial Launch Document. [online] Available at: www.utcolleges.org/media/15074/a5_flyer.pdf/ (accessed 11 September 2019).

University Technical Colleges (2019) About UTCs. [online] Available at: www.utcolleges.org/about/ (accessed 11 September 2019).

World Economic Forum (2018) Children in Singapore Will No Longer Be Ranked By Exam Results. Here's Why. [online] Available at: www.weforum.org/agenda/2018/10/singapore-has-abolished-school-exam-rankings-here-s-why/ (accessed 11 September 2019).

2. DEFINING A GENERATION FOR LEARNING

Critical issues

» **Understanding the changing timescale of a 'generation' in technological and educational terms.**

» **Appreciating the impact of technological change on society and learning.**

» **Understanding the future in terms of visions, challenges and opportunities.**

» **The paucity of government thinking in learning development.**

Talking about a generation

The purpose of this chapter is twofold. First, it explores the concept of a 'generation' as a technological concept in relation to the increasing rate of change in society. Second, it relates this term to a cohort of school pupils who will enter and leave formal education over the span of the next decade.

What is increasingly apparent is that the technological drivers of change in society are moving at an increasingly uncomfortable pace for many of us. Perhaps the most uncomfortable citizens in this drive forward are school pupils preparing for a future that is changing at a relentless pace. It is becoming increasingly clear that the body of knowledge their formal schooling has prepared them for is becoming gradually irrelevant (see Table 2.1).

How will we come to terms with a technological generation that is measured in so few years, when the educational generation is measured in decades?

THE TECHNOLOGICAL GENERATION

Forty years ago, a timeframe that was considered to be the span of a career in the world of work, there was an expectation that the whole of a working career may well reside within one occupation. You might change employers, and might experience redundancy, but the job skills you carried with you would largely see you through your whole career with some adaptations. A technological generation would constitute something like half or one-third of your working career.

If you worked on the railway, for example, as a driver or fitter, civil or mechanical engineer, you could comfortably accommodate the changes brought about by technological change. These may have been changes in the powering of locomotives, from steam to diesel to electric. The building and maintenance of the civil and mechanical aspects of the railway, although changing, were based on the same foundations and founding principles, with some increasing mechanisation included. Fundamentally, the railways involved you in an almost timeless series of jobs that were changing at the margins, although the central task of moving people and goods remained the same. Or so it seemed.

In the past few years, the move towards computerisation on the railways has removed one of the earliest and most vital roles on the system, that of the signalman. The thousands of signal boxes sitting at junctions and level crossings were manned, often for 24 hours a day. These are currently being reduced to some 10 central control boxes across the UK, connected by CCTV and remote sensors to every junction, crossing and controlling signal. This change is so profound that it is meaningless to consider 'signal operator' as a distinct and sizeable profession any longer.

The process does not end there. In trains, aircraft and automobiles, the direction of travel is to remove the human element from the operational loop. It is currently technologically possible to remove humans from the train cab, the airline cockpit and the driver seat of road vehicles. The only thing stopping these developments is the psychological impact on travellers of having no human in control; this, despite the fact that 'human error' is a component in a large proportion of accidents.

The car mechanic's career, to which so many young people aspired, was catered for through myriad apprenticeship courses. These were run by garages and technical colleges. Such a career was largely about applying general principles to new car models. The essence was getting your hands dirty and showing some artistry in tuning and fettling the vehicle to maintain optimal performance. Although there were changes in systems and performance, these could be accommodated because their adoption was generally gradual and measured.

However, the introduction of engine management systems in the past two decades has fundamentally changed the nature of the job, the skill set and the role of the car mechanic. No longer is the role one of 'engine detective', using all the senses to diagnose and fix the engine and components. The engine management system means the car no longer 'talks' to the mechanic. Today, the conversation is between the engine management system and the maintenance and systems computer. They hold an electronic conversation about what is wrong with the performance of the car and the appropriate remediation. The primary role of the mechanic is to respond to the result of this electronic conversation. Increasingly, that is simply to replace one malfunctioning or dead component with another.

This exclusion of the mechanic from the diagnostic loop is significant as it mirrors the direction of travel of the relationship between humankind and increasingly sophisticated machines. This is the artificial intelligence (AI) dilemma we shall all face eventually – functional redundancy. At some point, machines will overtake our skill sets.

Table 2.1 Changing jobs: job evolution driven by technology

JOB EVOLUTION DRIVEN BY TECHNOLOGY		
JOBS THAT HAVE DISAPPEARED, OR ARE NO LONGER SIGNIFICANT EMPLOYMENT OPPORTUNITIES, IN THE PAST 20 YEARS	NEW JOB DESCRIPTIONS CREATED IN THE PAST DECADE	JOBS EXPECTED TO DECLINE SIGNIFICANTLY IN THE NEXT DECADE
PRINT COMPOSITOR	WEB DEVELOPER	MILK DELIVERY PERSON
SIGNAL OPERATOR ON RAILWAY	BLOGGER	TAX COLLECTOR
SWITCHBOARD OPERATOR	APP DEVELOPER	LIBRARIAN
TYPIST	MARKET RESEARCH	FAST FOOD COOK
FILM DEVELOPER	DATA MINER	PILOT
BANK TELLER	SOCIAL MEDIA MANAGER	TRAVEL AGENT
DRAUGHTS-PERSON	INTERNET ENGINEER	POST PERSON
COOPER	LIVE STREAM ENGINEER	JOURNALIST
SECRETARIES	MICRO BREWER	SHOP WORKER/CASHIER
BOOK-KEEPERS	VAPE RETAILER	TELEMARKETER
	TELEMARKETER	

As an aside, an increasingly inappropriate preoccupation in the Department for Education (DfE) is in making a curriculum that mirrors this technological future. One development is in teaching information technology coding. But, in my view, the idea of adding coding as yet another element of the national curriculum, a kind of technological modern foreign language, is totally misguided. It is the equivalent of believing that you can create a world-class car industry simply by training everyone as a car mechanic. Understanding simple logic gates and the wiring associated with them might, of itself, be valuable knowledge, but the role of the coder is relatively low level when considered against the bigger picture roles in developing AI.

In fact, this simple, scalable, logical thinking is already a feature of current robotic technology, so it will not provide as many employment opportunities in the future. Indeed, my prior involvement in technological product developments highlighted that, when the big picture plan is developed, the simple coding task for individual elements is outsourced abroad to cheaper markets. In one case, this involved outsourcing to a former Russian nuclear submarine engineer. He had a large team of experienced coders who could turn round most well-specified coding tasks in a couple of days and for a few hundred dollars. This is not really the skill on which future high-worth, well-paid economies will be built.

Snapshots of the future

It was the car factory under Henry Ford that introduced the mass production process. It is now defining the cutting-edge world of robotics. The most startling thing about the modern car assembly plant is the absence of human beings on the shop floor. Human beings are not performing the primary assembly tasks anymore. Instead, they are monitoring the machines that complete those tasks.

It is in communication technology that the pace of change is fastest and here the mismatch between the future life experiences of pupils and the limited learning opportunities presented by their education will sell them short.

If you attended a major educational conference in 2009, be it a senior leadership event or a DfE-sponsored event with a Minister of State for Education present, there was a fair chance you would have been shown an engrossing and disturbing video that formed the quintessence of technical change. It was a peak into Pandora's Box. It was as enticing as the old future-gazing television programmes like *Tomorrow's World*. In characteristic style, the video was already two years old by the time the DfE started showing it. At least, at that time, they were trying to help put forward a dynamic view of the role of learning in the future world.

Underneath the cutting-edge 'the medium is the message' online production, there was an element of both challenge and menace in the accelerating rate of change and the impact it would have on society. In what some took to be a utopian future, and others took to be the foretelling of a dystopian nightmare, the presentation was called *The Machine is Us/ing Us* by Michael Wesch, Professor of Cultural Anthropology at the University of Kansas – and it went viral (Wesch, 2007).

At the time, it was a leading analysis of the change between Web 1.0, which required HTML to construct it, and Web 2.0, which enabled people to communicate without limit on the internet through social media. Now it already represents an essentially historic document. We have moved on so quickly.

Indeed, the presentation that characterised Web 3.0, the intuitive or semantic web, or the internet of things, which was at the edge of imagination when Wesch broadcast his seminal work in 2007, is now being overtaken by new, unimaginable and accelerating futures. A technological 'generation' has accelerated and is now considered to be less than five years.

By 2009, a new generation of defining ideas had arrived. A production called *The Future Internet: Service Web 3.0* tried to predict the direction of Web 3.0. It was both prescient and partially correct in its predictions. We miss the significance of accelerating technologies in our lives and education systems at our peril. What once were significant points in the landscape of our daily lives are now half forgotten memories. Who now remembers Myspace or Friends Reunited or even video shops? The educational knowledge of our children may, by the time they leave school, be completely redundant.

Current government thinking and the challenge facing us

Since 2010, in the UK under a Conservative government wedded to a policy of austerity, there is neither the concern, the appetite, nor the finances to address the issue of preparing pupils for the world of the future. As Michael Gove stated so starkly, 'we've heard enough from experts!' (Mance, 2016), thereby disengaging education from discussions of the future or even from a culture of reflection and development. The current interest is focused narrowly on outcomes, not processes.

These examples of technological and societal change are cited in some detail to illustrate the pace of change and the impact it is having on our lives and society. Such rapid changes in relevant knowledge and experience are not reflected in the curriculum nor the subsequent examination content or format. Only knowledge that can be tested in a formal written examination is deemed worthy of testing, thereby limiting the pupils' capacity to show the true range of their knowledge, understanding and abilities.

More disturbing is the fact that many of these and other technical developments have taken place in a timespan shorter than the school career of an individual pupil. What once was known as Moore's Law (Moore, 1965), which was an observation about the capacity and capability of transistors to double every two years, is no longer keeping up with the pace of technological progress. Exponential technological growth is reducing a 'generation of change' to a year. The event horizon warned of by Elon Musk (Holley, 2018) and others, when artificial intelligence becomes autonomous and is able to self-replicate and even seek to eliminate the irrationality of human beings, may not be so far away.

How then can we prepare pupils for a world that we cannot at present define, but which seems to be reinventing itself every five to ten years?

❖ Triangulation point

Consider the following questions in relation to your own school, or one with which you are familiar.

1. **With which skills for the future do you think your pupils are best prepared, and which areas are they poorly prepared for?**

2. **How well developed are your relationships with local employers and enterprises to ensure your pupils gain insights into the world of work through site visits and more extended work experience?**

3. **Do local employers provide 'real-life' learning/problem-solving opportunities, rather than class-based 'simulations' to enliven your curriculum?**

4. **Are there professional development opportunities available to you as a teacher/ member of the leadership team to experience the current world of work, through either secondments or shorter visits to local or national employers?**

5. **Has funding for careers/employment development for both teachers and pupils increased, decreased or stayed the same over the past five years? What impact has this had on morale, curriculum relevance and teacher competence?**

Summary

- The heavy hand of government, and the generally conservative nature of educational systems, means that the curriculum diet and skills development on offer in state schools are increasingly irrelevant and redundant.

- Taken with the examination system deficiencies discussed in the previous chapter, the inevitable conclusion is that we are educating the next generation for the life led by the last generation.

- Attempts to address these deficiencies, such as adding new components to an outmoded curriculum, are irrelevant.

- We need to completely review the purpose and processes the curriculum is designed to service if we are not to fail our young people.

Wesch, M (2007) *The Machine is Us/ing Us.* **[online] Available at: www.youtube.com/ watch?v=NLIGopyXT_g (accessed 11 September 2019).**

Mike Wesch's seminal explanation of the relationship between technological innovation and human interaction was much lauded when it was first published.

On the positive side, he outlined the great enabling force of the internet as a democratic tool. He developed his presentation, which was the ultimate manifestation of Marshall McLuhan's point about the medium being the message (McLuhan, 1964) at a time when the internet was in rapid transition. It was transforming from a tool that was so technologically sophisticated that it could only be accessed by technocrats speaking the native language of Hyper Text Mark-up Language (HTML), into a form of communication requiring no specific skills other than a keyboard and access to the internet.

This was the democratisation of the internet, insofar as the content of the web was no longer defined by those who could speak HTML; everyone could find a voice online through Web 2.0. The simplification of using the web and the growth of social media gave everyone access to the 'global village' (McLuhan, 1964), with social media hubs creating communities for social, political or economic interaction and education.

Wesch was very perceptive in seeing the direction of travel of the internet and anticipating some of the darker aspects of Web 2.0 and also Web 3.0. He could see Web 2.0 becoming a Tower of Babel in which all opinions contended for supremacy. When everyone can transmit an opinion, how do we differentiate between verifiable fact and unsubstantiated, but deeply ingrained opinion? Do we now live in a 'post truth' world in which the argument is won by the strength of feeling with which an opinion is expressed, rather than its veracity?

Equally sinister was the use of the internet by business. In a world in which your every online keystroke can be monitored, you provide your unique profile for the commercial world who can match their products to your desires. Alternatively, they may match your desires to their products by subtle manipulation and this may extend to material, economic and political wants and needs.

Web 3.0 is sometimes referred to as the 'semantic web' and the 'internet of things' and Wesch could see the creation of the internet leviathan that was not only responding to human users but using meta data, a quantity and quality of data previously unavailable, to anticipate needs in advance of their human expression. Projecting this development forward, we see the internet operating as a functioning brain, accumulating data and experience to be able to anticipate and execute actions. This is the genesis of artificial intelligence (AI).

To this extent, the term 'disruptive technology' is fully warranted as previous patterns of human interaction and social, economic, employment and political discourse are overtaken by developments online that shape the pattern of the future.

This is the backdrop against which young people will learn and live. This is why merely replicating existing redundant patterns of education is not tenable.

Robinson, K (2010) Changing Education Paradigms. *TED Talk*. [online] Available at: www.ted.com/talks/ken_robinson_changing_education_paradigms (accessed 11 September 2019).

This is possibly the most erudite and articulate exposition of the deficiencies that need to be addressed in the education system in the twenty-first century. Again, like Wesch's work, the medium in which the talk is presented presages how education generally, and learning more specifically, can be promoted in engaging ways using new technologies. This is the epitome of what an illustrated talk can achieve.

The main thrust of Robinson's talk is that the current systems of formal state education are incredibly wasteful of talent. The 'industrial process' of education is a quality control process designed to weed out any learners who do not conform to expectations at the end of production batches – the process wastes human potential we can ill afford to lose. Robinson argues for a system that is more collaborative, more relevant and more adaptive to rapidly changing circumstances.

Robinson's lament against the current state of education, and what is to be done about it, reflects the key issue of this book.

Bibliography

Holley, P (2018) Elon Musk's Nightmarish Warning: AI Could Become 'an Immortal Dictator from Which We Would Never Escape'. *Washington Post*. [online] Available at: www.washingtonpost.com/news/innovations/wp/2018/04/06/elon-musks-nightmarish-warning-ai-could-become-an-immortal-dictator-from-which-we-would-never-escape/?noredirect=on&utm_term=.a42e14322bf7 (accessed 11 September 2019).

Mance, H (2016) Britain Has Had Enough of Experts, Says Gove. *Financial Times*. [online] Available at: www.ft.com/content/3be49734-29cb-11e6-83e4-abc22d5d108c (accessed 11 September 2019).

McLuhan, M (1964) *Understanding Media: The Extensions of Man*. New York, NY: McGraw-Hill.

Moore, G (1965) Moore's Law. *Wikipedia*. [online] Available at: https://en.wikipedia.org/wiki/Moore%27s_law (accessed 11 September 2019).

Robinson, K (2010) Changing Education Paradigms. *TED Talk*. [online] Available at: www.ted.com/talks/ken_robinson_changing_education_paradigms (accessed 11 September 2019).

Wesch, M (2007) *The Machine is Us/ing Us*. [online] Available at: www.youtube.com/watch?v=NLlGopyXT_g (accessed 11 September 2019).

3. THE DEMISE OF THE KNOWLEDGE-BASED CURRICULUM

Critical issues

» Rethinking education by moving away from the closed education system and the primacy of the examination.

» Exploring international precedents in effective learning.

» The tyranny of the subject and the limitation of learning change.

» Defining the twenty-first-century learner: autonomous and independent.

Rethinking education: closed systems and international developments

The previous chapters have outlined deficiencies in the educational system. First, the educational system was considered as a closed system, operating in isolation from the world beyond its classrooms. This was an educational system defined by historical precedent that, by definition, was backward-looking and conservative. All national education systems, to some extent, have such a conservative element. This is because one vital element of a national educational system is to transmit the cultural DNA of the nation from one generation to the next.

Second, to do this, governments have a preoccupation with history and the elements that define the distinctiveness of the nation. These always form a key element in the curriculum offered to, or rather imposed on, pupils. In the UK, this includes the inordinate preoccupation with selected elements of national history, be these kings and queens and their partners or national figureheads. The telling of these national tales is highly selective; there is no attempt to be objective. This forms part of national mythology and cannot be sacrificed on the altar of evidence and interpretation. There is a focus on the 'great man' conception of history, so that industrialists, war leaders and scientists dominate and the people who toiled to achieve their accomplishments are underplayed.

In the relatively young country of the United States there are similar national preoccupations. These lead to rituals such as the Oath of Allegiance and disputes about the role of religion in state education. This is epitomised best by what was thought to be, but apparently is not, a redundant discussion of the role of creationism in the curriculum!

It is both inevitable and acceptable that the government which foots the bill for national education should also have some say in content. However, there is an increasing variance between national governments who seek to micromanage the curriculum diet of pupils, determining every aspect of what happens during the school day, and those who set broad features and key elements. They then leave education professionals to determine the building and delivery of that curriculum.

SYSTEMIC FAILINGS OF NATIONAL EDUCATION SYSTEMS

Surprisingly, education can proceed in many countries as an almost totally closed system – without reflection on the future for which they are supposedly preparing young people. A curriculum that is historically determined, and is increasingly at odds with the reality of society in which it operates, faces attrition and disappointment. These will be measured in three critical areas:

- the low morale and esteem of the teaching workforce, leading to recruitment and retention crises that threaten the national system;
- the 'unnatural wastage' of young people ejected, or removing themselves, from the education process as it proceeds;

- the mismatch between the knowledge and skills with which young people are equipped and the rapidly changing skills and competences required in the modern workplace, which compromise the employability of young people leaving education.

In England specifically, and the UK more generally, it seems as if the national systems are closed to meaningful change. The regulatory valve of the examination system is too late a point at which to recognise that the whole system has major systemic failures. These systemic failures to adapt and change at a rate commensurate with technological change on a globalised scale will compromise both the closed educational system and the societal and economic well-being that depend on it.

Clearly, more radical and comprehensive steps are needed if the English education system is to catch up with the needs of national society and the economy. Yet there is no great fundamental commitment to change in either society or the system.

THE EXAMINATION PROCESS: AN ENGINE OF EDUCATIONAL CHANGE?

The simplest engine of radical change would be to extensively reform the examination system. This would redefine the direction of travel of learning to a new destination, rendering past learning journeys irrelevant. However, too much is invested in the current examination system.

The A level is seen as the 'gold standard' for entry into the vaunted higher level of education. There are significant vested interests resistant to such examination-led change. Anything that challenges the A level is seen as dilution of the standards of the system (Weale, 2019a). Indeed the current debate regarding the introduction of the T level qualification, a vocational equivalent of A level, has fired up the argument regarding equivalence of academic and technical qualifications once again. Many in further education argue that this is the latest and unwelcome incarnation of a flawed approach to the problem.

Culturally, this has been the *de facto* purpose of the educational system – to whittle down pupils and discard them along the learning process until only those in possession of A level certificates were left. From these, the universities could select their undergraduates. It has always been a quality control process designed to refine and discard, and it has wasted so much young talent in the process.

Teachers have been complicit in this real-life winnowing of aspiration and opportunity, which is no more rigorous than the house-selection process at Hogwarts Academy. Indeed, the recent revelations of the cynical way in which academies have been 'off-rolling' pupils who are not going to contribute positively to their key performance indicators shows just how cynically young lives and aspirations are compromised for the sake of the prestige of the school and senior leaders (Weale, 2019b; Whittaker, 2019).

The kaleidoscope of competing political and societal agendas cannot conceive of a more appropriate learning model for the future. Nor can internal pressures for change in schools collaborate to design a better way of organising learning that is both more appropriate to the lives pupils will lead, and more in kilter with our economic and social aspirations for the future.

International precedents

Unsurprisingly, those countries in which education professionals have greater autonomy to determine effective learning tend to be higher performing and to have an educational workforce held in higher esteem in society. These are countries without recruitment and retention crises.

Finland is probably the most quoted example of such a national education system, but the other Scandinavian countries share similar profiles. Indeed, we may in future have to broaden the definition of Scandinavia to include countries like Estonia. Estonia has, through shrewd investment and a national debate about the role of the development of the country, made startling leaps up the OECD international educational effectiveness tables (Gurney-Read, 2016).

Significantly, the top performers in the Teaching and Learning International Survey (TALIS) table have not arrived at their vaunted status by standing still. They have invested in international educational research and in teacher development to ensure they are putting viable and ambitious learning programmes in front of their learners.

Finland and Singapore have specifically downplayed the importance of the traditional sit-down examination as an effective method to assess pupils. They are looking for a wider range of methods to capture the true potential and performance of the individual pupil. These will include the ability to work independently and collaboratively, to assess critical sources of evidence and to present ideas coherently.

A flavour of the direction of travel of Finnish education can be found in the course flyer presented by Suhonen (2017). Concern for the development of the individual pupil and a large degree of pupil-initiated, project-based learning characterise the Finnish system.

Meanwhile, Singapore is making a fundamental change in direction. Its previous rapid progress up the TALIS table has in part been down to rigorous testing and examinations, along the Chinese model of rote learning and high competition. Singaporean educators now recognise that traditional examinations do not present a comprehensive picture of the range of attitudes, behaviours and key competences required of the twenty-first-century learner. Their minister for education has gone so far as to say that the role of parents is to understand what puts the light in their children's eyes, rather than their position in the national tests, which will now be downplayed (Davie, 2018).

The tyranny of the subject and the limitation of learning change

Teachers have often been compliant in circumscribing their scope for innovation. Nowhere is this seen more graphically than in the tyranny of the subject department.

In secondary school, the subject is at the centre of what teachers train for. It is the focus of their daily teaching and it is the hub of each teacher's social and professional network in the school. It encourages an exclusive attitude to learning, which can be unhelpful to learners. It leads teachers to behave as if knowledge resides in discrete compartments, as characterised by the phrenologist heads so popular in the nineteenth century before research-led understanding became so popular (see Figure 3.1).

This commitment to subject-based learning is both inefficient and ineffective to learners. For example, in the course of their secondary education, pupils will come across at least four distinct operational definitions of the concept of evidence and proof. These will be applied respectively in science, mathematics, history and English. For the pupil, it is both confusing and unnecessary to provide four separate operational definitions for a single concept with four applications.

Departmental exceptionalism, by which the pressing demands of a particular subject for time, resource or control of definitions is more important than a unifying learning experience for the pupil, is the bane of the secondary school. It also promotes other aberrant behaviour. The teacher defined by subject knowledge and who adopts an undeserved professional research title is symptomatic of the teacher who has more regard for subject than pupils.

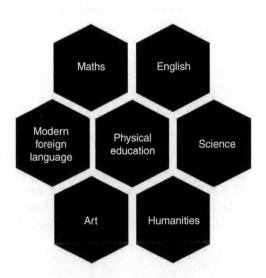

Figure 3.1 Old curriculum building blocks

I used to get animated when secondary school teachers used to refer to themselves as 'mathematicians,' 'physicists' or 'historians'... they were teachers of mathematics, physics or history. Had they been the former, they would be in universities or research institutes conducting research. As it was, they were meant, among other things, to be adequate communicators of their subject to learners.

Building a curriculum in which subjects are the building blocks undermines the quality of learning that takes place. It stresses difference where similarities would aid understanding. Most significantly, it prevents a unitary, whole-school culture to promote language and process learning to pupils. This is why the primary school system and structure of a teacher supporting the learning needs of pupils in a comprehensive way is more effective than the discontinuities in learning of the secondary school.

The traditional riposte has been that the complexity of learning at the secondary stage demands subject specialism. This is only true if we remain wedded to the idea that the main purpose of education is knowledge transfer. I would argue that twenty-first-century learning needs to be much more ambitious and wide-ranging if it is to produce young people able to survive and thrive in a rapidly changing and challenging world.

Case study

I remember one mathematics teacher entering the staffroom, declaiming, 'What is it with these children? I've taught them Pythagoras' Theorem six times now and they still don't understand it!' He seemed oblivious of the fact that he was outing himself as an incompetent teacher.

As I believe Einstein said, and I paraphrase... if you can't explain it to a six year-old, you don't fully understand it. I was reminded of this experience recently when talking to a former esteemed colleague and headteacher who had the same recollection of 'lofty physicists' indicating that their subject was the most difficult and pure of the sciences, and modern linguists who only wanted to be put in front of the top set!

Defining the twenty-first-century learner: autonomous and independent

A common refrain among educationalists and politicians alike is: 'How do we prepare young people for a future that we cannot define?' This is presented as an educational Gordian Knot whose insolvability prevents any meaningful and wide-ranging change.

This problem is only insoluble if you accept that the building blocks of education are defined solely in terms of knowledge. Not only individual gobbets of knowledge, but knowledge itself, or rather information, is the increasingly redundant element in the education equation.

Information is now ubiquitous. I can assemble more than 500,000 pieces of information on any given topic simply by typing a query into a search engine. Maintaining a complete educational system around the exclusive ability to hold such information in my head seems both redundant and arcane.

Much more important is the ability to interrogate that information, to test for reliability and to make new connections that are original and valid. The latter ability will define intelligence in the future, rather than the assembly of facts per se.

What does this mean for learning and the activities that go on in the educational establishment? Freed from a knowledge-driven learning model, new curriculum models with new building blocks are possible. Indeed, the metaphor of building blocks is appropriate here. Previous school learning models focused on preparing bricks of knowledge, with very few opportunities to assemble them into meaningful constructs. More forward-looking models can give opportunities to pupils not only to explore the raw materials of knowledge but to make imaginative and innovative constructions that meet real-world needs, solve problems or make original creative explorations (see Figure 3.2).

The departure point for this new learning paradigm must be understanding the pupil in the context of future challenges. That can only be addressed in terms of the attitudes to challenges, the learning behaviours and the underlying competences that will be required of the pupil in the challenging environment of the future. Knowledge is still important, but it is defined in terms of functional use rather than the accumulation of information. That Henry VIII was a king of England

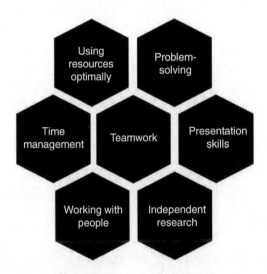

Figure 3.2 New curriculum building blocks

is less important that appreciating the impact his reign had on the social, economic and political development of the country. In mathematics, knowing how to measure and scale is of underlying importance to the application of that knowledge to practical problem-solving.

The picture painted here regarding the appropriateness of learning taking place in schools might be unduly harsh. There are, and always have been, innovative and passionate teachers in schools giving pupils access to first-class learning experiences which have applications to their aspirations and experiences beyond school.

Too often, however, these experiences and opportunities to experiment and engage in extended learning are the exception rather than the norm in the constipated knowledge-led curriculum. Here coverage is often seen as more important than quality of understanding. This is the GIGO (garbage in, garbage out) mentality of the examination system that values only those things that can be demonstrated within the confines of a formal time-framed examination.

Case study

I was often struck in schools where I worked by the concept of the annual 'Enrichment Week'. These were events when the usual school timetable was suspended and replaced by learning experiences assembled by teams of teachers, often based on cross-curricular themes. In some instances an adult visitor would have recognised a pattern of activity that was more akin to a primary than a secondary school. The enrichment activities were relentlessly engaging and exciting for pupils.

It seemed to me that if 'enrichment' was the successful learning going on in this one week… what was going on for the rest of the year? Or, to put it the other way, why was not every week enrichment week? Schools can be radical and innovative – they simply do not make it a high priority to focus consistently on learning quality. They seldom create time for teachers to collaborate beyond their departments on joint learning endeavours, unless it is sports day or a school play.

Too often teachers and senior leaders are deflected from this key learning purpose by concerns about uniform, punctuality, and behaviour management, as if these are concerns of equal importance to learning quality in the functioning of the school.

1. **In terms of professional development activities in the past three years, what proportion of time was given to:**

   - responses to national statutory requirements?

   - guest speaker-led awareness-raising sessions which may, or may not, have had implications for teaching and learning?

2. **In your own school, or one with which you are familiar, list the occasions when you have worked across departments on a joint learning project in the recent past. Were these joint endeavours successful for professional learning and for pupil learning outcomes?**

Summary

This chapter has examined the forces constraining educational change. It has shown that whereas publicly funded educational systems tend to be conservative in nature, teachers themselves work in 'traditional' methodologies and structures that limit their ability to reconsider and innovate or change learning models. The subject department structure of secondary schools epitomises a commitment to a knowledge-based system of learning delivery.

The ubiquitous nature of information, provided by the growth of the internet, means that the critical purposes and outcomes of education have to address a more holistic view of the learner in the twenty-first century. Countries deemed to have more effective educational systems internationally are already addressing these concerns. UK, and specifically English, schools are not yet reviewing their curriculum models in a radical and appropriate way to develop their pupils for the future. The implication of this failure to adjust will be felt in the social, economic and political welfare of the nation.

further reading

Organisation for Economic Co-operation and Development (OECD) (2019) *PISA 2018 Assessment and Analytical Framework*. Paris: OECD Publishing. [online] Available at: www.oecd-ilibrary.org/education/pisa-2018-assessment-and-analytical-framework_b25efab8-en (accessed 11 September 2019).

The OECD publishes a wide range of comparative data regarding the relative performance of educational systems by its contributory members. As the data is all gathered to a common research baseline, the results of their regular surveys are reliable as indicators of comparative performance of education systems internationally.

The survey that generates most attention in educational circles is the Teaching and Learning International Survey (TALIS), which often causes concern in political circles as it graphically outlines whether the national educational performance is improving or declining against other nations. This, of course, has major implications for international competitiveness and tends, in the UK, to promote expressions of concern about the 'must do better' verdict the tables invariably imply about the home countries' educational performance. As yet, the verdict of the OECD has not led to any major calls for a fundamental national debate, or reorganisation of the educational system to accelerate performance.

By comparison, in the key subject areas of reading, mathematics and science, other nations have made massive advances in performance in relatively short timespans. These have been achieved, generally, by adopting a more progressive attitude to teaching and learning, which is research-informed, teacher-led, and based on observation of what has been successful elsewhere. Estonia is often cited as an example of this progressive approach, which has led to rapid progress up the international comparative tables.

Bibliography

Davie, S (2018) Fewer Exams for Students, Less Emphasis on Grades. *Straits Times*. [online] Available at: www.straitstimes.com/singapore/education/fewer-exams-for-students-less-emphasis-on-grades (accessed 11 September 2019).

Gurney-Read, J (2016) OECD PISA Report: Where Does the UK Rank in the International School League Tables? Results in Full. *Telegraph*. [online] Available at: www.telegraph.co.uk/education/2016/12/06/oecd-pisa-report-does-uk-rank-international-school-league-tables/ (accessed 11 September 2019).

Organisation for Economic Co-operation and Development (OECD) (2019) *PISA 2018 Assessment and Analytical Framework*. Paris: OECD Publishing. [online] Available at: www.oecd-ilibrary.org/education/pisa-2018-assessment-and-analytical-framework_b25efab8-en (accessed 11 September 2019).

Suhonen, P (2017) Phenomenal Learning and 21st Century Competences in Finland. ALO Finland. [online] Available at: www.alofinland.com/news/phenomenal-learning-curriculum-competences/ (accessed 11 September 2019).

Weale, S (2019a) England's Post-16 Qualifications to Be Streamlined. *Guardian*. [online] Available at: www.theguardian.com/education/2019/mar/19/englands-post-16-qualifications-to-be-streamlined (accessed 11 September 2019).

Weale, S (2019b) More Than 49,000 Pupils 'Disappeared' from English Schools. *Guardian*. [online] Available at: www.theguardian.com/education/2019/apr/18/more-than-49000-pupils-disappeared-from-schools-study (accessed 11 September 2019).

Whittaker, F (2019) Spielman Ordered Sanction of Off-rolling School. *Schools Week*. [online] Available at: https://schoolsweek.co.uk/spielman-ordered-sanction-of-off-rolling-school/ (accessed 11 September 2019).

4. WHOLE-SCHOOL LEARNING INITIATIVES: FADS, GIMMICKS, STRUCTURES AND LEADERSHIP

Critical issues

» School-level traditions dictating learning practice.

» The lure of the magic bullet and INSET days in learning development.

» Building on solid principles: defining teaching and learning.

School-level traditions dictating learning practice

Much of the information in the preceding chapters has been concerned with 'big picture' issues related to national education systems, or glimpses of the challenges of the future. Although I eschewed the term in the previous chapter, these might be considered 'macro'-level considerations.

This chapter makes the transition from consideration of 'macro'-level issues to focusing on what happens in schools on a daily basis – 'micro'-level issues at the point where the education system delivers learning experiences to individual pupils. The chapter also concerns the limited way that schools make use of the expertise they already have to drive their improvement efforts.

The purpose of this chapter is to incite you, through what is essentially a provocation piece, to review your current arrangements for teaching and learning and examination preparation. It is focused particularly towards colleagues at secondary level but is equally applicable to tertiary level. Perhaps it is less pertinent to the experience of colleagues in the primary sector due to the holistic nature of the teaching. In the primary sector, support and development of the individual pupil as a learner tend to supersede the fragmentary nature of the curriculum offered in secondary schools and college settings.

The challenges of planning internal change

My opening observation is that, in the 200 or more secondary schools and tertiary colleges in which I have worked on some aspect of development, I have never seen a whole-school policy for teaching and learning that extends to the examination revision period. On reflection, I have not often seen a teaching and learning policy in a secondary school which sees the light of day on a daily basis and guides an improvement process.

There are reasons why there is such a wide gulf between policy and practice in secondary and tertiary sectors.

Perhaps the most pervasive is the unhelpful tradition that what happens within the confines of the classroom is considered the domain of the individual teacher. It takes a headteacher with a keen sense of purpose and a considerable appetite for resistance and conflict to focus significant development time on establishing 'improving learning in the classroom' as a fundamental plank of their development strategy.

There is always a lingering suspicion among staff that the headteacher may be motivated by a desire to 'monitor' staff as much as to improve classroom provision. It is an unfortunate implication, and a wasted opportunity, of almost 30 years of Ofsted inspection, that classroom observation is associated more often with the punitive aspects of inspection than with development opportunities that build upon the considerable best practice in the school.

Many schools experiment with new learning methodologies at the level of INSET events, involving charismatic speakers, outlining new and 'research validated' systems for transforming learning.

Headteacher sponsorship of the new learning approach means that considerable time, energy and resource are invested in embedding it across the school but, invariably, its impact declines rapidly over time.

The lure of the magic bullet and INSET days in learning development

The reasons why such approaches may fail over time are discussed below.

1. The use of an INSET day event to introduce a new process means that staff have no more than a superficial understanding of a new teaching and learning approach. An event that is meant to transform their lesson preparation and delivery inevitably leads to confusion, uncertainty and, for some, resistance as a defence mechanism.

2. Poor planning and auditing of teacher development time means that the new initiative is always considered as having to be introduced 'as well as' rather than 'instead of' all the initiatives and directives in which the teacher is already involved.

3. Inevitably, the new approach involves considerably more development time than that allocated, as teachers generate key implementation questions, concerns or points of failure.

4. Over time, there is the growing realisation that the new initiative was not the 'magic bullet' for learning that was described in the initial INSET experience. When both the headteacher and the staff realise this, the initiative is doomed. Unfortunately, the enthusiastic headteacher may cling to the belief that the initiative will work, given time, long after the staff have abandoned hope and commitment.

5. Without better and more inclusive systems for monitoring how change permeates through to the experience of the individual pupil in the classroom, such initiatives do not have a quantitative or qualitative basis for assessing their effectiveness. The initiative may be abandoned at the point where it is yielding a positive impact on learning. Or leaders may persist with it when any effective data analysis would reveal it was having no positive impact on learning outcomes or pupil engagement.

6. The fact that the idea was an external one, imported whole and designed to fundamentally change classroom practice, creates tensions in the school. Some teachers would be resistant to any change to their current and essentially comfortable practice. Many more would welcome an opportunity to extend their professional practice and effectiveness but are given little time for professional engagement and reflection on how, jointly, they can improve the diet they offer pupils. The initiative implementation masterplan marginalises such teachers and, ultimately, brings them frustration rather than professional growth.

7. The distance between the senior leadership team and staff will exacerbate all the above elements. If the school is rigid and hierarchical in structure and outlook, then ownership of the project, no matter how worthy, will always reside exclusively with the leadership team. Opportunities to discuss, improve and refine the project can be lost in the 'top-down' implementation process.

The range of such educational 'magic bullets' presented as learning panaceas over the past two decades has been overwhelming. Few schools will not have dabbled in at least one of the following initiatives, which Ross Morrison McGill characterises – perhaps uncharitably, perhaps not – as 'learning fads'. He assesses the impact of them as falling into one of five categories: myth, hearsay, fad, gimmick or, more positively, 'the jury is still out' (McGill, 2019).

I present them in Table 4.1 as a kind of 'initiative bingo'. Any completed line, down or across, wins a prize, with the bumper jackpot for any teacher who can claim they have taken part in every initiative on offer! A row is left blank at the bottom of the chart for any initiative you have encountered beyond the 20 mentioned.

Table 4.1 Initiative bingo

THINKING HATS	RAPID PROGRESS	PERSONAL LEARNING THINKING SKILLS	ZERO TOLERANCE	TEXTBOOKS
LEARNING OUTCOMES	CHINESE TEACHING	BRAIN GYM	FOUR-PART LESSONS	ASSESSING PUPIL PROGRESS
DETAILED LESSON PLANS	STARTERS, MIDDLES AND PLENARIES	GROUP WORK	TEACHER TALK	VERBAL FEEDBACK
VERBAL FEEDBACK STAMPS	SITTING IN ROWS	TRIPLE MARKING	ASSERTIVE DISCIPLINE	LEARNING STYLES

McGill's conclusions, if valid, suggest that the imposition of external learning initiatives on schools may be compromised by the research basis of the new approach, as much as by the flawed way in which they are implemented in schools.

Meaningful change in learning design and pupil learning outcomes clearly needs greater external validation, along with increased internal reflection and professional conversations and monitoring to embed and become part of the culture of the school.

Building on solid principles: defining teaching and learning

To have an effective teaching and learning protocol requires some clarity and shared and agreed understanding of what constitutes effective teaching and learning. Only on such a firm foundation can the learning experience of pupils be improved in a rational way.

Case study

A WORKABLE TEACHING AND LEARNING TEMPLATE

I have broken the ground on this issue of teaching and learning with leadership teams so many times! Often I have been engaged to promote a particular theme, such as the incorporation of new learning technologies to individualised learning, or from new curricula to assessment to performance management. The conversation often took the same route. The headteacher was keen to add a new direction/initiative onto the existing systems in the school without recourse to more fundamental considerations, of which teaching and learning was usually the most significant. In truth, they had often been sold the features of a new approach, rather than the tangible educational benefits.

In these circumstances I would always try to steer the conversation back to how the new initiative/direction would impact on learning. What changes would it make to the way the teacher and support staff would go about their business in the classroom? If they could not produce a clear rationale relating the proposed new initiative to classroom practice and the experience of learning opportunities offered to pupils, I would suggest that this was either not the right initiative or not the right time to implement it.

Suggesting they did not proceed with an initiative they had engaged me to develop often produced consternation. I would turn the discussion to more fundamental issues to ensure they had a clear rationale for implementing or rejecting the new initiative. This would relate to their core task of promoting better teaching and learning outcomes. This list tended to produce a more constructive dialogue about uniformity of improvement across the school.

Teachers should:

1. have clear objectives for each lesson, which reflect the needs of all the pupils;
2. make the learning experience engaging and challenging, where possible relating it to real-life experiences;
3. make the learning experience as practical as possible so that the lesson engages the senses and allows pupils to move around and engage in discussion;
4. model positive attitudes and behaviours to learning so that they become accepted and acted upon as part of the learning repertoire;

5. ensure that there is an element of risk-taking in the learning experience so that pupils can experiment with approaches, experience failure or sub-optimal performance and reflect;
6. have an effective plenary so that pupils can analyse their own performance and learn from that of others;
7. ensure that teacher talking time is as short as possible and that pupils' voices dominate discussions;
8. have fun and allow pupils to make mistakes and react positively.

The difficult part is ensuring these guidelines are employed consistently to give the pupils a quality assured learning experience which prepares them to be an autonomous, independent learner.

A headteacher without a guiding vision of the key processes within the school is difficult to deal with. However, just as tricky is the evangelist who has a new educational theory as a guiding light.

A short history of the impact of new learning initiatives

Certainly, the past two decades have seen a plethora of new educational fads gain ground. Some are based on sound research, but many are not (Education Endowment Foundation, 2019).

Then came 'learning styles': a bastardisation of some serious neuroscientific research, which had pupils assigned to a particular learning style, based on some spurious analysis. Books were distributed in colour sequence to indicate that a pupil was a visual or auditory learner so that the teacher could differentiate and pitch their lesson as inclusively as possible. This was a laudable personalisation aim, but offered a spurious structure to achieve it.

Raising standards has often been associated with the production of detailed lesson plans, so much so that the writing of these plans sometimes overwhelmed teachers to the extent that they were spent forces once in actual contact with the pupils! I remember, when I first started teaching, hearing horror stories from other young teachers that, in their schools, a senior manager would call in the planning books on Monday morning and any anomalies or missing lessons would have to be explained in a formal interview with the headteacher. What an oppressive and compliant atmosphere to create.

Add to this list the other fads that have gained ground, such as simply reproducing the rote learning characterised by Chinese schools, Thinking Skills and Thinking Hats, Brain Gyms, Starters, Middles and Plenaries and a veritable tsunami of external approaches that have shaped the thinking of school leaders. Each approach has some value in helping to define significance and structure in learning. Unfortunately, none provides the universal panacea for learning improvement on the path to excellence. Worse, being external solutions, they undermine the native expertise within the school.

There will undoubtedly be educational research, particularly in the areas of neuroscience and brain plasticity, which will have a significant impact on the way teachers go about designing learning experiences. New approaches like these will embed most successfully in schools that have mechanisms to absorb and disseminate such research. The school cannot swallow external findings whole, without having mechanisms in place to evaluate them, and transform them into workable and sustainable programmes to inform the planning and delivery of learning (Herold, 2019).

I am arguing here for the school to become a synaptic learning organisation. The synaptic school would be one that, just as the brain functions, can filter ideas and signal them to key groups so that the pattern of understanding and experience in the school develops organically. The concept of the synaptic school is developed further in Section B of the book.

Case study

ZERO TOLERANCE AND ASSERTIVE DISCIPLINE

The most pernicious initiative I have encountered, in terms of damage done to effective teaching and learning in schools, is 'assertive discipline' with its zero tolerance approach.

This suspends learning activities in the classroom and seeks to create the optimum disciplinary control of pupils. The underlying assumption is that effective learning cannot take place until there is discipline in the learning space. It is a superficially enticing proposition, but really puts the cart before the horse in terms of how it skews classroom conditions towards the imposition of discipline rather than learning activities.

It has a superficial and erroneous notion of discipline, which suggests you can modify behaviours simply by imposing the same rewards and sanctions consistently. It ignores context and relationships, has no nuance and demands that disciplinary issues, the awarding of rewards and the imposition of sanctions dominate the learning time.

The extensive ring binder that accompanied the programme outlined in tremendous detail how the teacher would manage the classroom for uniformity. As all teachers would have their initiative taken away by the programme, the result would be the uniform application of performance expectations and standards on all pupils, in all circumstances. This would lead to pupils complying with organisational expectations.

The failure to make eye conduct, speaking when the teacher was talking and failing to stay on task all lead to a suspension of any learning taking place while the teacher formally issues the sanction and tells the pupil how they are disrupting lessons. The teacher may decide to escalate the sanction and involve detention, or, in the worst cases, a duty teacher coming to remove the errant pupil to a place of isolation.

The problem with the place of isolation is that it is full of other errant pupils who are looking to buck the system. The school is now committed to a full academic week of teachers to staff the isolation room and to remove pupils from class and take them to the isolation room. Although my experience of this assertive discipline programme approach goes back some two decades, it is a live issue again in UK schools, with isolation booths and a policy of 'flattening the grass' coming to characterise the practice of a number of multiple academy trusts (MATs) (Dickens, 2019).

The assertive discipline/zero tolerance programme came as a bought-in training day and set of materials. I think the initial educational research, which all such programmes claim by way of credibility, must have been conducted in the US penitentiary system, or in a modern incarnation of Pavlov's dog's laboratory!

Certainly, I became aware of a direct relationship between the sumptuousness of the teacher folder given out in such programmes, together with a term's worth of 'customised for your school' sanction and reward cards, and the uselessness of the programme.

The worst aspect of this initiative was that the focus on learning was completely lost in the process of implementing assertive discipline and both staff and pupils became increasingly disillusioned with the whole process (Education Support Partnership, 2019).

Change structures in schools

Schools carry a heavy burden of cultural expectations about how things should be done, which are unhelpful to systematic improvement.

THE FOCUS ON DIFFERENCES IN LEARNING INHERENT IN SUBJECT DEPARTMENT AUTONOMY

I speak to secondary schools here when I state that subject departments are given too much leeway in development time to complete predominantly administrative tasks.

Essential, whole-school initiatives are compromised by the exceptionalism that insists they take a secondary role to the priorities of subject departments. 'It is a good idea, but unfortunately it does not reflect the issues and priorities of the science/mathematics/English/humanities department' has seen the demise of many a whole-school project.

Learning effectiveness should always trump the parochial priorities of the individual department if the school is serious about sustainable improvement.

❖ Triangulation point

1. For your own school, consider the initiatives that have been developed (or imposed) and reflect on and account for the factors that have made them a relative success or failure in the long term.

Summary

This chapter has focused on the school as an agent of change. We have considered how schools take on new ideas, and the way in which they are often enticed by fashionable initiatives, which they are ill-equipped to implement.

Leadership and structural deficits account for these failures.

Schools tend to be underdeveloped in structures to identify and share existing internal experience and to absorb effectively the best ideas of external research.

But do not despair! The synaptic school, in which reflection in, and on, practice, sharing experiences and testing new thinking in learning, is a possible way forward from the current position.

Bibliography

Dickens, J (2019) 'Flattening the Grass': What's Really Going on at OGAT and Delta? *Schools Week*. [online] Available at: https://schoolsweek.co.uk/flattening-the-grass-whats-really-going-on-at-ogat-and-delta/ (accessed 11 September 2019).

Education Endowment Foundation (2019) Teaching and Learning Toolkit. [online] Available at: https://educationendowmentfoundation.org.uk/evidence-summaries/teaching-learning-toolkit (accessed 11 September 2019).

Education Support Partnership (2019) Helping You: Resources. [online] Available at: www.educationsupportpartnership.org.uk/resources?f%5B0%5D=field_type%3A42&gclid=EAlaIQobChMIq5e30-LN4gIVTbHtCh1mYADkEAAYASAAEgLS6PD_BwE (accessed 11 September 2019).

Herold, B (2019) Education Has an Innovation Problem. *Education Week*. [online] Available at: www.edweek.org/ew/articles/2019/01/09/education-has-an-innovation-problem.html (accessed 11 September 2019).

McGill, R M (2019) 20 Years of Educational Fads. *Independent Schools Portal*. [online] Available at: www.independentschoolsportal.org/uploads/5/0/2/1/50211243/20_years_of_educational_fads.pdf (accessed 11 September 2019).

5. FROM EDUCATION TO LEARNING: WHAT THE PUPIL BRINGS TO AND TAKES FROM THE LEARNING PROCESS

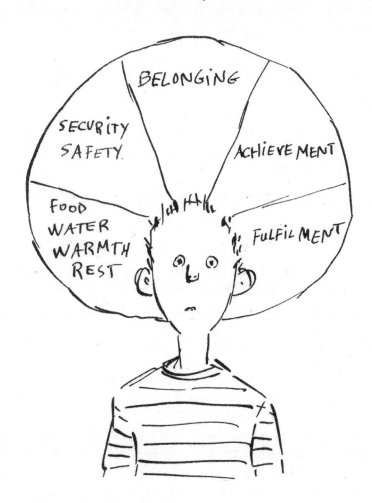

BELONGING

SECURITY SAFETY.

ACHIEVEMENT

FOOD WATER WARMTH REST

FULFILMENT

Critical issues

» The difference between the education given and the learning received.

» The individual pupil's perspective of learning in school.

» A hierarchy of learning needs to be addressed and a model to address them.

Defining the interaction between the education system and learning experienced by the individual

In the preceding chapters, there has been an unwritten assumption that the direction, tone and content of education are set centrally, which they are. However, to understand education as a simple response to central diktat builds a false understanding of what happens in schools on a daily basis. Any teacher can tell you that what happens in the interactions between pupils and the teacher and teaching support assistant on any given day is a more sophisticated and nuanced set of interactions than can be encompassed by central policies developed by government.

If we were talking about economics, we would be making an essential distinction between macro- and micro-education. Macro-education is developed at the centre, at the level of policy; micro-education happens daily in schools and influences the education received by individual pupils.

The educational process is far more sophisticated than economics, however. The relationship between cause and effect, or input and output, in the educational process is far more complex. This is because every single policy is filtered through the efforts of every single teacher and is received differently by every single pupil. If this was not the case, we could apply the managerial approach to learning decried in the first book in the series, *Future-Proof Your School*. We could assert, with some certainty, that by merely assembling resources, we could maximise the learning outcomes of every pupil in a particular cohort. The management of learning could be completely controlled by managerial processes of inputs and outputs. But this is not so, and we need to explore the relationship between the educational experience provided and the learning experience received by individual pupils.

As it is, despite the fact that whole-year cohorts in schools receive essentially the same education in lessons, they do not produce a uniform series of learning outcomes. The flawed analysis of Burt, considered in Chapter 1, would suggest the spurious conclusion that the reason for the variation in learning outcomes across the year cohort was simply one of variation in intelligence.

It is far more complex.

From education to learning: the pupil experience

Essentially, every pupil receives a different education, because every pupil has a different receptiveness to the educational experience offered to them. To summarise, education is predominantly a process of transmission, be it from central policy to school or, in classrooms, from teachers to pupils. How receptive the pupils are to the educational experience, and how effectively they are influenced by it, is a completely different process called *learning*.

This section is not designed to give a comprehensive analysis of the myriad factors impinging on the ability of pupils to learn effectively. It merely signposts some of the main classifications of factors that limit the progress pupils can make on their individual learning journey. It is hoped that teachers will look more deeply at the way pupils present themselves in class, and develop a keener understanding of the issues that might have influenced their particular patterns of behaviour.

As an aside, the issue of behaviour management in schools is often presented as the imposition of the will of the teacher over the collection of pupils comprising the class. This chapter suggests that a more meaningful, positive and less abrasive relationship can be developed by responding to individual pupils in a more receptive and individual way.

As my American colleague Professor Darleana McHenry so aptly put it: 'The kids need to know you have skin in the game, that you will do everything in your power to support them and that you always have their interests at heart.' As the teacher, you are not a passive observer in their successes and failures but an active participant, turning their failures into successes. This level of commitment to your pupils is the greatest guarantor of continuing success and, at many times, the most difficult commitment to uphold. A pupil with a teacher-advocate who will coach, support and develop them and also defend their interests as a learner with powerful potential has a priceless champion. That teacher does not need to maintain discipline in the class. They will have inculcated self-discipline in the pupils, such that the weight of the teacher's disappointment is a heavy burden for the pupil to bear. Doing the right thing, being kind and thoughtful, sharing and taking pride in their work become internalised behaviours.

Critical facets of pupil development and experience

Even so, the teacher needs to recognise that each pupil brings to their learning a range of attitudes and behaviours that reflect their prior experience. Their relationship with positive learning habits might not be well established, they might not yet have the emotional maturity to cope with learning, let alone learning independently. They may have been discouraged from developing positive learning habits by poor role models in the home or in their community. They may have conditions that compromise their learning abilities, which need addressing before they can develop autonomous learning habits and behaviours.

Indeed, they might be homeless and insecure, which may compromise their sleep, security and self-worth and make engagement with learning almost impossible (Digby and Fu, 2017).

All these factors demonstrate why the teacher whose first concern and motivation is the subject might motivate the pupils initially but will never consistently develop the potential of all in the class.

Rather than develop a long list of limiting factors that need to be overcome before the pupil can move towards becoming an independent and autonomous learner, let us classify them into broad headings. Although this classification helps to organise our thinking, it should be remembered that pupils might present with multiple learning issues. Indeed, for those conditions recognised as autism spectrum disorders, the picture might be a multilayered, complex picture of issues and subsequent needs.

What follows is not a complete overview of major academic, clinical or medical disciplines. It is merely a scaffold of key ideas to be addressed if a school is to be effective in meeting the learning needs of all its learners.

PHYSIOLOGICAL FACTORS

The learning receptiveness of the pupil is determined by a wide and diverse range of factors. These factors may be physiological. They are particularly important influences in teenage years when periods of rapid bodily change and growth, and the hormonal triggers underlying them, impact on emotional stability, temper regulation, concentration and sleep.

Physical impairments such as vision, hearing and co-ordination deficits also mean that a pupil will, without appropriate support, be unable to derive the maximum benefit from the educational experiences provided. For those with known learning disabilities, all the key factors may be exacerbated by the nature of the learning disability (Judith Trust, 2019).

Physiological factors may be permanent or transitional but will need addressing if the pupil is going to maintain progress as a learner. Conversely, the pupil with an acute condition may find that their learning in the school setting is interrupted either temporarily or for much longer timespans. Liaison with other agencies engaged with learning outside school, such as hospital schools, social services and adoption agencies/charities, is required both as the pupil leaves the school setting and on reintegration in order to maintain learning continuity.

PSYCHOLOGICAL FACTORS

More generally, chemical imbalances may be at the heart of psychological conditions; these might impinge on the pupil's ability to effectively receive and benefit from the education provided. Individual pupils may not be able to interact with others with appropriate emotions and behaviours, or even with any response at all.

There is much debate regarding the classification of conditions such as autism and attention deficit disorders as to the physiological or psychological basis of their origin. This further complicates the learning picture.

Certainly pupils experiencing acute psychological conditions need particular specialist support, as well as wider understanding from across the school community. Without such support, the structures within schools might lead to a psychological condition being superficially recognised as 'challenging behaviour'. Then the default school response becomes to send the pupil down the rabbit hole of 'disciplinary procedures', which might ultimately end with the pupil's exclusion.

SOCIAL FACTORS

The receptiveness to the education provided is also influenced by social factors.

One should never underestimate the power of peer pressure on influencing the pattern of behaviour of young learners. The desire to conform and fit in is a powerful motivator in young lives, while self-expression and the maturity to 'know their own mind and preferences' are still developing (Lyness, 2015).

The age of the internet, although barely two decades old, has produced as many problems as it has wonderful learning opportunities. The pervasiveness of communication technology means that young people are often described as being in '*a constant state of partial concentration*' (Wikipedia, nd). Projections as to the long-term impact of such a state do not suggest a happy and fulfilled individual will emerge from this age.

Beyond the psychological impact of such persistent use of these technologies, there is a social impact. The association of social media with negative behaviour patterns is revealed in incidences of online bullying, 'happy slapping' and behaviour conditioning. In more than one instance, these have had fatal consequences (O'Keeffe and Clarke-Pearson, 2011).

There is a sense of a paradox in 'social' media: there are few other avenues which have the ability to leave the individual more socially isolated and feeling inadequate from the false images of success and sociability the media presents (Ehmke, 2019).

Case study

I was recently contacted through social media (a communication media I strongly recommend should be strictly limited and controlled by serving teachers!) by a pupil I had taught in my first teaching post in rural Cambridgeshire. She was widely regarded in the staffroom as a 'difficult' pupil. Moody and petulant, given to cutting comments and temper outbursts, she was not an easy person to move forward in learning.

I never knew what had made the experience of her teenage years so turbulent, whether it had been personal circumstances, a heady and toxic hormonal load, or a combination of the two. The causes of her behaviour might have been instructive in coming to an understanding of her behaviour. However, on a lesson-by-lesson basis, I was more interested in moving her considerable native talents forward.

I quickly found one technique that did not work, and that was to praise her in front of the class. I remember vividly an occasion when, in the flow of a discussion, she made a characteristic and particularly telling comment which anticipated a point I was going to make several stages forward in the discussion.

'Well done,' I said. 'I think that is a particularly important point which gets to the core of the issue!'

As I turned to record it on the board I heard her say, not as a quiet aside, but as a direct challenge: 'I don't care what you think.'

Given that I was teaching history, I was able to deflect her petulance by replying: 'I think you are right to be sceptical of what I say. Anyone who is serious about history has to be prepared to interrogate their sources and look for accuracy or bias, and that is as true for anything I state as for written documents. However, we don't always need to state out loud that we are sceptical, we can simply think it and proceed accordingly.'

I faced her directly as I said this so she was aware I had acknowledged her challenge and had addressed it, without escalating my response. This was the point at which I managed to avoid entering a spiral of challenge and counter-challenge.

At the end of the lesson, I asked her to stay for a minute to review the incident. As the outburst had taken place near the beginning of the lesson, there should not have been any residual anger left by this point. I asked her if I had inadvertently said something that had upset her, or whether she had brought the anger into the lesson from an earlier incident?

I had not expected her reply, which was that I had shown her up in front of the class by praising her. She made it very clear that praise did not accord with her self-image. She knew she was clever and did not need a teacher to show her up by pointing it out. I apologised and explained this had not been my intention and that we should both go away and try and come up with a different way forward if verbal praise was so painful for her. She seemed almost frustrated that I did not intend to escalate the incident further by imposing a detention.

I came up with a possible solution a few weeks later when she made another telling verbal observation. I simply nodded in acknowledgement and moved on. When the class were engaged in written and discussion work, I discreetly slipped a short note onto her desk thanking her for her comment and suggesting where she might take her idea forward. Nothing was said then or subsequently so I assumed that this was a more acceptable form of praise for her. I used the technique regularly up to her GCSE examination – in which she performed to a very high standard.

The reason I mention this incident from more than 30 years ago now is that the first thing the former pupil said to me on social media all those years later was to apologise for her awkward and aggressive behaviour and to remind me of the little paper slips I used to give to her. To be honest, I had forgotten the paper slips, until she reminded me. She said that she had greatly appreciated my efforts and that she had kept and treasured every note. I was pleased to hear that she had indeed fulfilled her potential and is leading a happy and contented life.

Of course, over time, my recollection of the incident might be slightly unreliable. She may not have been quite so polite in her interjection, it might have contained considerably more 'expressive' language. Similarly, I might not have been quite as decisive as the text suggests in coming to a measured solution to the problem at the time. Nevertheless, the general points remain true and similar incidents are faced every day by teachers in classrooms.

I tell this anecdote, which has universal resonance with teachers, to illustrate a critical point: no pupil enters a classroom without baggage.

If they are lucky, and have had a happy and fulfilled childhood with love, support and a wide range of learning opportunities, the baggage will become useful, equipping them to undertake many varied and wondrous learning journeys with increasing independence.

If less fortunate, pupils may not have experienced such rich emotional support or learning, or may have been unable to access them because of some psychological, medical or physiological deficit. For these pupils, the baggage they bring will weigh heavily on them, and make learning progression a slow and tortuous process.

A hierarchy of learning needs to be addressed

Returning to wider considerations of learning effectiveness, the contention of Burt, and those who followed the logic of his model into the tripartite educational system, was that intellectual ability was, essentially, genetically predetermined. It could, therefore, be tested by a spurious examination at age 11. Why test at all if ability is genetically predetermined? Surely the educational qualifications of the parents would be all the evidence required to establish the right of the pupil to their birth right of a place in grammar schools?

Burt's blunt and spurious model took no account of innate ability and social mobility. Indeed, despite the claims of its protagonists, the grammar school system is probably the surest impediment to social mobility. It guarantees the vast majority of prized places to those who already enjoy considerable social advantage by virtue of the educational and social standing of their parents.

The wider selective system emphasises a process of rationalisation that is weighted heavily in favour of previous generations who have already enjoyed its benefits. It is a deficit system that penalises further those without social advantage and justifies this waste of educational talent on spurious predetermined intellectual grounds.

If this 'intellectual predetermination' model is so flawed, what can replace it in ensuring that each pupil receives support to reach their learning potential?

The work of Maslow has much to commend it as a model around which to organise a comprehensive education. His model of a hierarchy of needs, first postulated in 1943 and developed through several expansive reiterations since then, has many quality assurance aspects associated with it. Initially concerned with a hierarchy of human needs, it can be developed equally as a basis of learning needs (see Figure 5.1).

One of its greatest strengths is that it is not a deficit model. It does not categorise human beings by what they allegedly cannot do. It is a positive model that explores the conditions required for humans to flourish in life and, I propose, in learning.

In an educational sense, merely applying the basic Maslow model gives valuable insights into what is required to ensure that each individual pupil can make a success of their education. School leaders could apply the model to the circumstances of their own school to establish what they need to do to create the conditions for universal success.

For example, pupils who come to school hungry, sleep deprived or without secure and habitable housing will not be well prepared to give the best account of themselves in an educational setting. This is a live issue in the United Kingdom generally, and in England specifically given the rising indices of all these forms of deprivation.

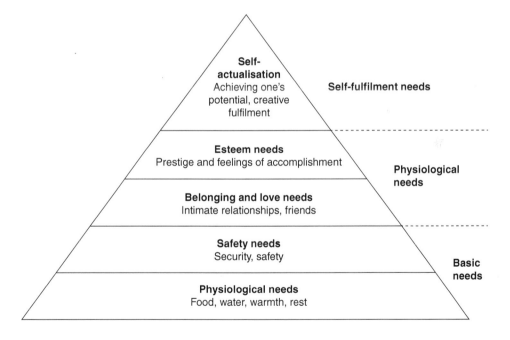

Figure 5.1 Maslow's hierarchy of needs

Source: Maslow (1943)

1. How does the Maslow model of needs resonate with the structures in your own school for meeting pupil needs?

2. Which elements of pupil support do you consider to be most and least well developed in your school? How would you explain this pattern of development?

3. How would you characterise the level of interaction with other agencies providing support to children to ensure your pupils receive 'wrap-around' provision to maximise their learning potential?

Summary

This chapter has moved the focus away from the national drivers of education, and even the cultural drivers at work within your own school. It has focused exclusively on the factors motivating, or inhibiting, the learning of individual pupils in your care.

A hideously complex picture has been presented simplistically in order to promote some fundamental reflection on what your school offers pupils. Pupils' needs have to be considered explicitly from first principles, relationships and support structures if you are to overcome the difficulties, and maximise the learning potential, of each pupil.

In subsequent chapters, this pupil-centred perspective is further addressed.

further reading

Maslow, A H (1943) A Theory of Human Motivation. *Psychological Review*, 50(4): 370–96.

Maslow's seminal work on the hierarchy of human needs was first published in 1943 and has since been amplified and built upon by Maslow and other commentators.

The model has had a pervasive influence in psychology because it eloquently spans both personal and social psychology and is applicable to any community, social, workplace or whole society. Indeed, the modelling of industrial and commercial organisations around the concept of a hierarchy of needs which bring meaning and empowerment to the job has had a primary influence on the development of what was once the personnel department. In large organisations personnel has morphed to the current nomenclature of the 'human resources' department and 'talent acquisition' roles in companies. This reflects a more rational understanding of the ability distribution in the population and the need to secure and develop talent as an act of self-preservation and development.

Surprisingly, the model, even in the simpler original form, has not been much applied to educational settings. I use it in this chapter to provide an opportunity to provoke a truly fundamental review of what schools do in relation to the needs of their pupils. The culture they promote, the support they provide, the interpersonal relationships they develop and the learning experiences they foster can all be encompassed in the model.

Furthermore, the model builds on human requirements for all lives to flourish, rather than ideas based on the predetermined and rationed spread of so-called 'ability' that characterises too much of the activities of schools, specifically, and education more generally.

Bibliography

Digby, A and Fu, E (2017) Impacts of homelessness on children - research with teachers. *Shelter*. [online] Available at: https://england.shelter.org.uk/__data/assets/pdf_file/0011/1474652/2017_12_20_Homelessness_and_School_Children.pdf (accessed 11 September 2019).

Ehmke, R (2019) How Using Social Media Affects Teenagers. *Child Mind Institute*. [online] Available at: https://childmind.org/article/how-using-social-media-affects-teenagers/ (accessed 11 September 2019).

Judith Trust (2019) Social, Psychological, Emotional & Physical Issues for People with Learning Disabilities. *Judith Trust Website*. [online] Available at: www.judithtrust.org.uk/learning-disability-and-mental-ill-health/social-psychological-emotional-and-physical-issues/ (accessed 11 September 2019).

Lyness, D (2015) Peer Pressure. *Kid Health*. [online] Available at: https://kidshealth.org/en/teens/peer-pressure.html (accessed 11 September 2019).

Maslow, A H (1943) A Theory of Human Motivation. *Psychological Review*, 50(4): 370–96.

O'Keeffe, G S and Clarke-Pearson, K (2011) Clinical Report: The Impact of Social Media on Children, Adolescents, and Families. *American Academy of Pediatrics*, 127(4). [online] Available at: https://pediatrics.aappublications.org/content/127/4/800 (accessed 11 September 2019).

Wikipedia (nd) Continuous Partial Attention. *Wikipedia*. [online] Available at: https://en.wikipedia.org/wiki/Continuous_partial_attention (accessed 11 September 2019).

6. ATTITUDES, BEHAVIOURS AND COMPETENCES FOR THE FUTURE: WHY WE CANNOT DELIVER THEM

Critical issues

» Why the government acts as an inhibitor of educational innovation.

» How the TALIS international educational effectiveness tables redouble failed methodologies in UK schools.

» Lessons from abroad: developing practice in Finland and Singapore.

» Re-engineering the curriculum from first principles and trusting the professional judgement of teachers.

Template for the future learner

The previous chapters considered a range of forces and pressures either promoting or inhibiting changes to learning in schools. They are recapped here to gain some clarity regarding what learning for the twenty-first century should encompass, and which elements of current learning models must be sacrificed to achieve a modern relevant curriculum.

As ever, when substantial changes to the curriculum are mooted, everyone seems to have a clear view of what they want in the new curriculum. Unfortunately, there is much less consideration, if any, to the process of slimming down the curriculum to ensure that what is taught is coherent, relevant and deliverable in the time constraints under which teachers work.

THE DEAD HAND OF GOVERNMENT IN EDUCATION AND LEARNING

We have seen how governments generally, given that they meet the cost of public education, have a view and demand a say in the content of the curriculum. Governments are less effective at promoting effective educational models for the future. This is for a number of reasons, outlined below. Governments are better at securing a place in the curriculum for what they consider the cultural DNA of the country; the history and cultural drivers of the country's development. Of course, few countries are self-confident enough to include failures and negative aspects of the country's past in this heavily edited picture of continuous improvement and heroes and heroines.

Governments also recognise the relationship between education and economic success and are keen to promote the latter by interventions in the former. Unfortunately, their interventions tend to be simplistic and unconsidered. Exacerbating their interventions is the annual publication of the Programme for International Student Assessment (PISA) results by the Organisation for Economic Co-operation and Development (OECD). The Teaching and Learning International Survey (TALIS) tables show what amounts to effective performance internationally in the key areas of reading, mathematics and science education.

Politicians have the desire to imitate the performance returns of Finland, Singapore or even Estonia in these key performance areas. Nonetheless, they apply a central command system of increasing statutory requirements and the narrowing of the curriculum to what are considered the key performance areas of literacy, mathematics and sciences, to the detriment of other subjects.

This goes against the pattern of development of the top performing countries, where educators are moving away from a high-stakes testing regime and are looking to teacher professional development to bring improvements in learning.

Finland and Singapore, in particular, have moved to greater pupil expression and self-supported, independent learning through extended project work. This provides a more appropriate range of experiences in which the pupil can develop and display broader skills and competences. It also provides more realistic learning settings than simulation exercises from textbooks in the classroom.

The issue with government interventions in England specifically is that they are politically motivated and results driven. These points alone explain their failure.

Since the election of the minority Conservative government in 2010, the underlying driver of all their public service policies has been 'privatisation'. This has been a compulsion of the right wing of the party since the days of Margaret Thatcher. It is a cultural belief that the 'market' can deliver results more effectively and more efficiently through private companies driven by profitability.

In education, the 'juggernaut' to push this view forward has been the Academy Programme (West and Wolfe, 2018). Much of the school estate has been transferred to academy chains who have brought an 'industrial' ethos to schools which stresses data management, inputs and outputs – all the elements previously attributed to the process called 'managerialism'. Managerialism is the belief that any concern, be it education, health and social care or even the protection of the realm, can be reduced to a series of inputs and outputs.

The role of the manager is to minimise the inputs and maximise the outputs so the results will be high performance at low marginal cost. From transport to public utilities, social care to the prison service and even the preparations for the 2012 London Olympics, this has lamentably failed to be the case. Despite this, the mantra continues: private ownership is good, public ownership is bad.

In education and healthcare, the worst aspect of privatisation has been the marginalisation of expertise in the school system. I may be accused of overplaying the comment of Michael Gove in his statement that 'we've heard enough from experts', but it expresses perfectly the marginalisation of educational professionals in the rush to academisation. The ending of the Building Schools for the Future programme in 2010 saw the abandonment of sound educational research informing learning development. For example, research on the learning space of the future was abandoned for a set formula for classroom size which allocated each pupil a standardised space and then multiplied it by 30 to arrive at the standardised classroom. There has never been such a government-sponsored paucity of educational vision.

Managerialism, and the privatisation of education that it promotes, has had three unfortunate consequences in driving English education since 2010.

- First, it excludes educational professionals, with their experience and expertise, from participating fully in the debate about the priorities and directions of the educational system in the UK, generally, and in England, specifically.
- Second, it takes little to no account of educational research into effectiveness and school improvement. Consequently, it is not progressive and developmental, and is always designed to be reactive to the latest data or crisis.
- Third, it promotes short-term, results-oriented answers to long-term development questions.

The failure of the UK to make the required progress up the TALIS tables has brought the response of sacrificing the 'broad and balanced' curriculum. Previously this 'broad and balanced' curriculum has been the agreed foundation of what pupils would learn for several generations. Now, it has been replaced with an increasing preoccupation with English, mathematics and science at the expense of all other subjects (Richardson, 2010). The curriculum is less rich and broad than it was in English schools and the wider funding crisis provoked by austerity has further marginalised the place of the arts and languages in schools (Whittaker, 2018).

Lessons from abroad: developing practice in Finland and Singapore

Had the government looked in more depth at the methodologies used by Singapore (Zainalabiden, 2017) and Finland (Transfer Wise, 2017), they would have seen that their spectacular performance was not arrived at by government diktat. Instead, Singapore and Finland established a national debate about learning aspirations for the future to ensure national prosperity and personal fulfilment. Similarly, the experience of teachers in Hong Kong is developed through a key-values-driven philosophy (Cheung, 2015).

Once the national debate had established the core values and priorities, it was left for educational professionals to weave these strands into a coherent plan. They deliver this through an appropriate, challenging, inclusive and coherent research-informed curriculum. Moreover, the role of the teacher is highly valued in these countries. It is well compensated and developed with what, in the UK, would be considered 'outrageous' amounts of training and development support (Kayange and Msiska, 2016).

The missing links: a template for change

However, the deficiencies in English education cannot be remedied simply by appropriating the best practice from these international examples.

Teachers in England do need to develop more professional independence. They need to become more reflective of their own efforts within their school. They also need to be more informed by educational research regarding pedagogy, heutagogy and the appropriate use of educational technology to promote greater educational efficiency and effectiveness. This would enable them to provide pupils with more appropriate and challenging learning experiences. However, all these teacher concerns are necessary, and not sufficient, conditions in the search for a curriculum of excellence and learning delivery models which inspire every pupil.

Figure 3.2 in Chapter 3 presented the building blocks for a curriculum to equip learners of all ages for the twenty-first century. In contrast to the building blocks of the current curriculum, which were subject blocks designed to promote knowledge transfer, the new curriculum building blocks are all based on attitudes, skills and competences. The key change required to access this new learning paradigm is to understand that the key feature of effective new learning is not knowledge, but the individual learner.

Consequently, all the paraphernalia associated with the knowledge-based curriculum is also redundant. The sit-down examination, the obsession with testing, the artificial distinction between the learning in the course and the process of revision, the silo blocks of knowledge, the teaching methodologies, the pupil as the object and not the subject of learning, assessment protocols and the physical and mental restrictions of the standardised learning space and time must all be abandoned too.

This would appear to represent a change as profound as the Cultural Revolution in the People's Republic of China in the 1960s. In many respects it does but, unlike the chaotic implications of that historical event, in education such a radical redesign would have purpose, momentum and direction. These are all the things that the National Professional Qualification for Headship (NPQH) informed me were essential leadership dimensions when I completed the qualification in 1999.

How can such profound changes be accomplished in schools?

Case study

BUILDING SCHOOLS FOR THE FUTURE: LESSONS LEARNT

When involved in the Building Schools for the Future (BSF) programme between 2008 and 2010, I supported schools to develop a strategic vision for their rebuilding. The Academy Programme, underway then, was guided by placing additional resources and concentrating new builds in areas of greatest social deprivation rather than by a privatisation drive. Potential academies were encouraged to partner with local organisations to ensure that the curriculum would benefit from access to real-life learning opportunities in the field and, potentially, through mentors from local organisations who would help drive aspirations and career pathways. I was proud to have been party to developing some phenomenal pieces of new thinking in learning.

At one transforming school, we worked extensively with the local National Health Service Trust. One aspect of curriculum development was that it would address the high incidence of poor health in the area.

A high-specification gymnasium with extensive community access was to be part of the new build. The gym and other areas of the school were to be equipped with heart-monitoring equipment so that pupils could both understand the link between exercise, diet and healthy living and generate 'live data' to inform mathematics and science lessons. Statistical interpretations, graphs, percentages and probability were still taught, but now in a much more engaging and personal way.

The link between health and diet was emphasised by the development of an extensive allotment on the school grounds. This was in part developed by local market gardeners. They supported the development of the raised beds and techniques for the growing of vegetables. The whole process was underpinned by a 'mini-enterprise' designed to grow food to sell to the school kitchen at prices that ensured sustainability. Dieticians from the Trust helped in decisions about what to grow and what appeared on the school dinner menu to maximise healthy living. The mini-enterprise approach provided 'hands-on' experience in enterprise, entrepreneurship and accounting for pupils.

The mentoring roles included work experiences in the local Trust, on hospital wards, in administration and in the community. Indeed, the community came into the school, as a clinic was provided there to help the improvements in pupils' health percolate into the wider neighbourhood.

Although the example of impactful curriculum innovations outlined above took place within a major capital programme, they illustrate what can be achieved through partnership, shared resources and new thinking. The major costs were time and commitment.

All the examples could proceed without massive changes to the process and constructs of learning in the school. To that extent, although it had a fundamental and positive effect on the commitment and enthusiasm of pupils, it represented less than a full commitment to a twenty-first-century education.

This begs the question addressed in the following chapter: what would an education for the twenty-first century look like and how might it be designed and implemented?

❖ Triangulation point

1. To what extent does the local business community engage with your school? Does it provide funding, facilities or expertise to develop your school-based curriculum provision?

2. There have been tremendous changes to both 'careers education' and opportunities for pupils to benefit from work experience placements. How developed is the provision in your school and what could be done to improve it?

3. What low-cost, high-impact activities could you engage in to revitalise your curriculum through community engagements?

Summary

This chapter has brought together elements discussed in previous chapters to produce what at first appears to be a bleak landscape of opportunities lost in redesigning the education pupils experience in English schools.

Selected international examples have been used to illustrate more enlightened attitudes to designing a curriculum fit for the twenty-first century.

However, this chapter has contrasted the dead hand of government on 'education' with the innovation in 'learning' that accompanied previous national initiatives. Whereas the government controls education provision nationally, there remains considerable scope for innovation in learning that rests with individual school leaders, teachers and the community.

Further reading

Organisation for Economic Co-operation and Development (OECD) Education Department. [online] Available at: www.oecd.org/education/ (accessed 11 September 2019).

The Organisation for Economic Co-operation and Development (OECD) Education Department reports provide the most accessible database of information, reports, country profiles and comparative data analysis about all the main aspects of education development.

The main comparative exercises are the Programme for International Student Assessment (PISA) reports and the Teaching and Learning International Survey (TALIS) analysis. Effectively, these two reports provide, from a common baseline, international comparative data about the relative effectiveness of national education systems in terms of outputs.

Behind the comparative data are useful reports about either common aspects of learning in key subject areas, or country profiles which explore the direction of travel of learning in particular countries.

Bibliography

Cheung, R (2015) Hong Kong's Teacher Professional Training Programme Needs Fine-Tuning. *South China Morning Post*. [online] Available at: www.scmp.com/lifestyle/family-education/article/1748656/hong-kongs-teacher-professional-training-programme-needs (accessed 11 September 2019).

Kayange, J and Msiska, M (2016) Teacher Education in China: Training Teachers for the 21st Century. *The Online Journal of New Horizons in Education*. [online] Available at: www.tojned.net/journals/tojned/articles/v06i04/v06i04-24.pdf (accessed 11 September 2019).

Richardson, H (2010) Gove Puts Focus on Traditional School Values. *BBC News Online*. [online] Available at: www.bbc.co.uk/news/education-11822208 (accessed 11 September 2019).

Transfer Wise (2017) The Finnish Education System: An Overview. *Transfer Wise*. [online] Available at: https://transferwise.com/gb/blog/finnish-education-overview (accessed 11 September 2019).

West, A and Wolfe, D (2018) Academies, the School System in England and a Vision for the Future. [online] Available at: www.lse.ac.uk/social-policy/Assets/Documents/PDF/Research-reports/Academies-Vision-Report.pdf (accessed 11 September 2019).

Whittaker, F (2018) The 6 'Major Risks' to the Quality of Education, According to Ofsted. *Schools Week*. [online] Available at: https://schoolsweek.co.uk/the-6-major-risks-to-the-quality-of-education-according-to-ofsted/ (accessed 11 September 2019).

Zainalabiden, F (2017) The 6 Changes to Singapore's Education System MOE Announced Today. *Must Share News*. [online] Available at: https://mustsharenews.com/singapores-education-system/ (accessed 11 September 2019).

7. THE CHALLENGE OF THE FUTURE: PEDAGOGY, HEUTAGOGY AND DANGEROUS ASSUMPTIONS

Destined to fail   Destined to struggle   Destined for greatness.

Critical issues

» Exploring the critical need to abandon the content-led curriculum for a model more in keeping with the twenty-first century.

» Challenging and remodelling assessment.

» Building a curriculum from the needs, talents, interests and requirements of the individual pupil.

» Changing the culture and operational practices of schools to ensure that every pupil thrives and works with an expectation that their talents will be recognised and nurtured.

The challenge of defining the future

Teacher-led musings regarding the future of education are often prefaced by the remark: 'How can we prepare pupils for a future that we cannot know and which does not yet exist?' This is lazy thinking which is profoundly unhelpful.

We are perfectly aware that the future is going to be a place where change, due to technology, is going to happen at an accelerated rate. We know that communications technology is ubiquitous, as is the knowledge that continues to define current education models. This knowledge is available, anywhere and anytime, from any mobile device connected to the internet. It would be perverse to build the whole of a pupil's experience in education around selected elements of information they could obtain for themselves from their mobile device.

THE INCREASING REDUNDANCY OF THE KNOWLEDGE-BASED CURRICULUM

Expressed this way, it becomes perfectly clear that the knowledge-based curriculum, with a terminal examination to test the acquisition, retention and recall (ARR) of selected items of that knowledge, is inappropriate now, and will be redundant in the future. Summative assessment of this sort, as a filter for determining success and failure using a quality control model, is increasingly wasteful of the precious talent our young people possess. It defines the success of some by the failure of the many.

What then will replace it? The answer is both challenging and exciting.

Clearly, we need building blocks of learning which will equip pupils for the future and ensure that the curriculum they receive in schools equips them for committing to lifelong learning as a critical process beyond school. One body of knowledge, no matter how comprehensive, will not endure through their working life. Indeed, the more comprehensive the knowledge base developed in schools, by definition the more superficial the level of understanding the pupils will have.

Undoubtedly pupils, once beyond the formal school system, will need to return to learning when their current knowledge base is overtaken by events, advances in new technologies and artificial intelligence (AI) or when they want, or need, to change direction in their life. This may be because of either internal drivers or external factors. In many respects, this is already the case.

For the last two generations, education commentators and business have been proclaiming 'lifelong learning' to be the educational path for the future. But this has not led them to propose fundamental changes to the school curriculum in order to embed this feature. However, they have merely considered the need for a learning component beyond school, a commitment to a 'learning refresh', initiated by events such as redundancy or personal growth and interest (see Figure 7.1).

If automation, new technologies and AI proceed at the current predicted rate, then massive swathes of the population will find themselves with a redundant skills set and the need to retrain. Nor will this be confined to those easier to replace manual jobs that have been at risk, or replaced, since the start of the industrial revolution. This is not a sectional concern for the least skilled in society. It concerns us all. The educational system is the only effective mechanism to address this impending crisis.

There will be greater clamour for change when the middle classes, traditionally the bastions of support of the current school and examination system, find that the 'professional' jobs to which they aspire are not immune from the tsunami of computer technology.

The job of an accountant will be replaced by an algorithm, which chooses the optimal pathway of decisions for best financial outcomes. The job of the medical researcher can be replicated by a diagnostic machine, which reproduces tests against given criteria, with absolute precision, avoiding the element of human error.

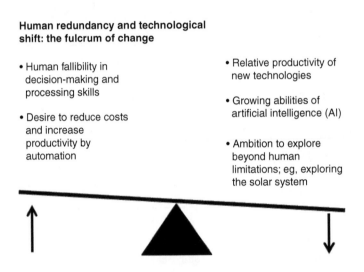

Human redundancy and technological shift: the fulcrum of change

- Human fallibility in decision-making and processing skills

- Desire to reduce costs and increase productivity by automation

- Relative productivity of new technologies

- Growing abilities of artificial intelligence (AI)

- Ambition to explore beyond human limitations; eg, exploring the solar system

Figure 7.1 The fulcrum of change

failing to meet learning needs: the learning experience of pupils during revision

If the curriculum content is redundant, what will replace it?

Certainly, we need a more comprehensive set of tools to promote learning excellence for all. This must be appropriate, quality assured and therefore personalised to meet the learning needs, strengths and weaknesses of each individual.

Once we start to personalise learning, to differentiate the way we set out learning challenges for individual pupils, as teachers have been urged to do for at least three decades, then the delivery of the curriculum becomes critical. The nature of the learning space, class size and the timing of the learning unit need review.

Clearly, we cannot afford to waste the talents of our pupils through a quality control rationing of academic success. Neither can we fail to equip our young people to be able to thrive in a rapidly changing society, economy and environment. To do so would be morally reprehensible and economically disastrous. The ethics and superstructure of the new learning paradigm must be rational, quality-driven and inclusive.

ASSESSMENT: CHANGING WHAT IS VALUED TO CHANGE BEHAVIOURS

In turn, the nature of the role of the teacher is thrown into sharp relief in this new learning landscape.

As in any organisation, teachers conform to, and focus their efforts on, the key organisational drivers. At the same time, they are resistant to any proposal for change that seems to deflect them from their key purpose.

In schools, the most influential behavioural driver is the assessment system. This is because the measure of the effectiveness of the teacher is related to how many pupils successfully negotiate the examination system.

The written summative examination drives and proscribes what happens in classrooms on a daily basis; it could not be otherwise. Any proposed change to the curriculum will have little impact if the examination system remains unaltered. If we wish to contemplate fundamental change to the curriculum, we must also encompass fundamental change to the assessment system.

It is the failure to embrace changes to examination assessment because of spurious commitments to a 'gold standard', 'rigour' and an alleged 'level playing field' that has prevented English education making incremental rather than sustainable improvements to pupils' achievement.

Such changes, which government ministers often describe as 'fundamental' or 'radical', seldom go further than replacing a numbering system with a letter-based system, or vice versa for grade levels. Indeed, such is the abiding compulsion with what is considered the top level of abilities that the grade that has seen the greatest attention has been the top grade, with an A* category added to differentiate between pupils in the top percentiles.

How then can the assessment system be reformed, and what will be the impact on the curriculum?

The starting point for this analysis must be two key definitions. One will be familiar to teachers, and one is less familiar.

Pedagogy:

Noun: pedagogy; plural noun: pedagogies.

The method and practice of teaching, especially as an academic subject or theoretical concept.

This has been the dominant aspect of education delivery from the times of Aristotle. For our concerns, the most important element, and limitation, of the term is that it is concerned exclusively with learning as a one-way process from teacher to pupil.

Pedagogical models make no allowance for the individual pupil. Underlying pedagogy is the idea that all pupils are equally receptive to the professional prowess of the teacher to deliver the knowledge in an engaging way that the pupil can acquire, retain and recall for the examination.

Equally corrosive to the effectiveness of the learning process is the influence that pedagogical approaches have on the focus of the teacher. With the focus exclusively on what the teacher is doing and not what the pupils are learning, lesson-based teaching can become a *performance*, rather than an activity in learning effectiveness. We all have tales of remarkable teachers who engaged us in learning through dramatic tales, explosive experiments or wondrous creative art extravaganzas. Indeed, we aspire to be the teacher who former pupils will recall at their reunions as having made learning memorable.

Obituaries for teachers habitually recount their 'love and passion for their subject' as a high plaudit, such is the steely grip of pedagogy on practice in the classroom. How effectively they motivated and influenced their pupils to achieve worthwhile and fulfilling careers and lives seems incidental to their role, if mentioned at all. Although there will always be an element of 'performance' in the repertoire of the teacher, we are not, after all, *actors*. Our commitment should not be to our performance, but to the learning of the pupils of every aptitude, attitude and ability put before us. This is why maintaining the exclusive focus on pedagogy cannot move learning, and the wider education system, forward in the direction and pace required to be deemed nationally or internationally effective in preparing for the disruptive future we face.

Heutagogy:

Noun: self-determined learning.

Heutagogy (based on the Greek for 'self') was defined by Hase and Kenyon in 2001 as 'the study of self-determined learning.'

It is hardly surprising that the term heutagogy is so unfamiliar to teachers. Despite its classical antecedents, it has only become current since Hase and Kenyon coined it in 2001. Unsurprisingly, the term did not grow naturally out of the closed system of educating children, but from a study of the education of adults (andragogy) in vocational settings. This study suggested that successful learning with adults was more often associated with the learner having greater autonomy and self-determination in the learning process.

Given the changes brought about by information and communication technologies (ICT) in the past 30 years, even the youngest pupils are now autonomous users of computer applications on their mobile phones or other devices. We have moved through three generations in the past 20 years. Internet users have been successively exposed to:

- Web 1.0 passive searchers in the information ocean and expertise of others;
- Web 2.0 authors to an international audience through social media;
- Web 3.0 users with an almost symbiotic relationship with technology whereby our interests generate new content tailored and personalised to our needs and desires in the intuitive web and the internet of things.

These seismic shifts in the way we access and digest information have taken place within the timescale in which a child is born to the point that they leave full-time statutory education.

FACETS OF INDEPENDENT AND AUTONOMOUS LEARNING AMONG PUPILS

If further confirmation was needed of the ability of untrained and 'uneducated' young people to access, use and learn autonomously, from computer-based application, without adult intervention, the most dramatic example is revealed in the 'Hole in the Wall' experiment of Professor Sugata Mitra (2013).

Mitra and his colleagues made a hole in a wall in a rural suburb of Delhi, characterised by high levels of social deprivation. Into the hole was placed a computer. No instructions or guidance were provided as to its use, but local children approached the machine and started exploring with it. Very shortly, they had mastered the basic operation of the computer, and were using it in increasingly sophisticated ways to build their own understanding of topics that interested them.

In many respects, this is the purest form of heutagogy. There is no adult intervention or direction, or rather interruption, to the self-determined learning engaged in by the individual child. Significantly, these unbridled demonstrations of heutagogy did not occur in the formal educational setting of the school, but when the children were left, literally and metaphorically, to their own devices.

Although children in the UK demonstrate similar patterns of heutagogical self-determined ICT usage in their everyday life, once they enter school and become pupils, their learning autonomy is severely constrained. Autonomous learning is not generally valued in school and is seen as disruptive of the dominant pedagogical model and pre-eminence of the teacher as leader of learning. Indeed, in many schools, access to, and autonomous use of, personal technologies in lesson time constitutes a disciplinary offence.

Paradoxically, there is an underlying assumption that possessing an ability to work independently is a function of personal maturity and innate intellectual capacity. Surveying teachers would give the impression that it is a capability more often found in girls than boys. There is no conception that becoming an independent and autonomous learner is something that can be taught. There is no drive to develop the capacity to learn alone successfully because the sheer weight of curriculum knowledge that needs to be transferred to the pupil precludes this.

Despite this, as pupils approach their statutory examinations at age 16, they move from a pedagogical and teacher-led learning model in the classroom to study leave and revision. Left to their own devices, it is unsurprising that so many pupils are unable to deploy a fully formed range of heutagogical techniques to manage both their learning and time effectively in the run up to examinations.

The revision process itself makes a startling number of assumptions about a pupil's home learning environment. A quiet and purposeful place to study is a basic requirement that not every pupil will possess. Recent evidence of the number of pupils in temporary accommodation, which is wholly unsuited to family needs, or in transit between temporary accommodation, highlights the size of the problem in England (Wainwright, 2018). The issues related to homelessness or home insecurity are not confined to basic human needs; they take a toll on adults' and children's mental health as well (Shelter, 2019). To these numbers can be added those whose education is disrupted by chronic illness and/or hospitalisation.

A further category of pupil, doubly disadvantaged by the examination system generally, and the revision and study leave component in particular, are those who have special educational needs and/or disabilities. This involves a large group of pupils with a vast range of conditions which makes access to education more difficult. If their needs have been recognised, documented and statemented, they will receive additional support, often in the form of one-to-one help to negotiate learning. This is a rare and precious resource and is usually overstretched. Such support, of course, will not be available in the period of study leave. Even when schools have bowed to government pressure not to grant study leave, the quality of the support pupils receive in the run up to and during the examinations is often compromised. This is due to the appropriate teachers not always being available and, as the examinations begin, pupils not being able to attend the full programme of revision.

Those whose additional educational needs have not been diagnosed or supported through their years in school will be doubly disadvantaged.

By way of compensation, those with a permanent or temporary special educational need and/or disability can claim some relief in the actual examination. Even so, extra reading time, more time to write, or even an amanuensis, to help record answers in a written format, are hardly adequate compensation for a lost revision programme.

The seemingly outrageous statement in the introduction regarding examinations embodying the structured failing of pupils seems less so in this context.

The quest for personalised learning: methodologies and assessment

How the teacher manages the progress of individual pupils, setting them different learning challenges and then assessing their development progress, requires a leap of two generations in thinking.

In truth, the challenge to personalise learning and provide appropriate and challenging pathways for each pupil in the class has proved almost impossible under current assessment models and expectations. If the dominant learning model is teacher-led and exposition heavy, there is not time for the teacher to give the individual support required of meaningful personalisation.

There has been an expectation that learning technologies, from interactive whiteboards to learning management systems, would provide a pathway by which the existing pedagogical model could buy more time for the teacher to provide more pupil-level support. Unfortunately, due to poor and incomplete training and sub-optimal understanding of the potential productivity improvements that the new technologies provided, these have failed uniformly to give teachers more time to work differently in class.

In truth, we should not be surprised by this. As long as the dominant lesson delivery model is teacher exposition to a class of not fewer than 30 pupils, the time benefits derived from use of learning technologies are going to be limited, regardless of the merits of the individual technology.

Personalisation will rely not only on different teaching methodology, but also on a different method of assessment which focuses on the individual pupil.

This will not be a summative model. It will not be based on grading against marks out of ten linked to external criteria that are not explained fully to the pupil prior to the commencement of learning. Assessment will not even take place through a shared understanding of the assessment criteria and a mentoring role, the formative assessment model. Instead, the pupil will be encouraged to take responsibility for their learning progress as an equal partner, and the fundamental challenge will be to improve on best previous personal performance – an ipsative role in which the teacher acts as coach.

Clearly, we need to be able to understand both assessment criteria and the effectiveness of the various models presented. A summary table is provided in Figure 7.2 below.

Assessment model	Visualisation as learning model	Teacher/pupil learning relationship
Summative assessment Tests that evaluate how much someone has learned throughout a course by a formal written test taken at the end of the course.	Pedagogy 	Teacher determines time, place, style, content and pace of the learning in a standardised lesson format. Pupil is largely a passive recipient of learning with occasional opportunities to answer questions.
Formative assessments Tests that are taken during the course and enable the teacher to diagnose learning achieved and gaps in understanding and remediate.	Refined pedagogy 	While maintaining a class-based teaching model, the teacher makes time to check the learning of individual pupils in a mentoring model.
Ipsative assessments Tests are based on the pupil looking to be intimately involved with the assessment process. The intention is for the pupil, like an athlete, to improve on their previous best performance. Criteria to describe and rate improvement need to be developed.	Heutagogy 	The pupil determines the pace and direction of own learning. The teacher works with each individual pupil, in a coaching model. The aim of each coaching session is to help the pupil determine how to improve on their previous best performance against a shared assessment criteria which has statement and quantitative elements.

Figure 7.2 Assessment models and their related teaching models

❖ Triangulation point

1. **For your own school, consider the impact of new learning technologies. Find examples where it has:**

   - transferred what was going to be done anyway into an electronic format; for example, using an interactive whiteboard to display a PowerPoint presentation that, otherwise, would have been written on the original whiteboard without any appreciable improvements in learner engagement or learning outcomes;

   - allowed the teacher to be more effective in delivering feedback, thereby negating the need to hand-mark a set of books with feedback, only accessed by the pupil in the following week's lesson, by which time it is of no developmental value;

   - given pupils access to the technology to scaffold, work collaboratively, or present to a peer audience a report of findings for critical appraisal.

2. **Consider the relationship between your mainstream and special educational needs and/or disability (SEND) provision.**

- Do subject teachers understand and modify their approaches to pupils with SEND requirements? What evidence do you have that SEND pupils perform to their potential in the terminal examinations?

- How does your SEND provision prepare pupils for the period of autonomous and independent study represented by the revision and study leave period?

Summary

This chapter reconciles the organisational methods of current education provision with the increasingly insistent demands for change required to meet the challenges of the pace of future developments.

I have painted the current pedagogical model of educational delivery in schools as being in an unstable state. Despite claims of providing a 'level playing field' across the span of a pupil's engagement in secondary school, and in their preparations to take the GCSE examinations in particular, the current system institutionally disadvantages a significant proportion of pupils.

I have proposed an alternative heutagogical learning model both as a solution to this institutionalised unfairness of current provision, and as a methodology that repurposes education to prepare pupils much more systematically with the skills, attitudes, behaviours and competence needed to face a challenging future.

Bibliography

Hase, S and Kenyon, C (2001) Moving from Andragogy to Heutagogy: Implications for VET. *Graduate College of Management Papers*. [online] Available at: www.researchgate.net/publication/37357847_Moving_from_andragogy_to_heutagogy_implications_for_VET (accessed 11 September 2019).

Mitra, S (2013) The School in the Cloud. *TED Talks*. [online] Available at: www.ted.com/speakers/sugata_mitra (accessed 14 June 2019)

Shelter (2019) One-in-Five Adults Have Suffered Mental Health Issues in the Last Five Years, Due to Housing Problems. *Shelter*. [online] Available at: https://england.shelter.org.uk/professional_resources/housing_and_mental_health (accessed 11 September 2019).

Wainwright, D (2018) Homeless at Christmas: 'How Will Santa Find Us?' *BBC News*. [online] Available at: www.bbc.co.uk/news/uk-england-46360119 (accessed 11 September 2019).

Section B
BUILDING WITH AND FOR PUPILS: AN INCREMENTAL APPROACH

Section A concerned itself with transforming learning on a whole-school basis to promote learning excellence more widely. It assumed the senior leadership team and governors were ready, and able, to fundamentally review all aspects of the learning experience of the pupil.

Not all schools are in a position to contemplate such massive changes to their culture and way of working. They may consider that circumstances are not right, resources are not available, or staff and governors are not committed to such change. To the extent that others have already made such giant leaps of faith and commitment to future learning, they are potentially wrong in this assumption. However, there are costs to being early adopters of new ideas. These perhaps introduce elements of risk that leadership teams are unwilling to bear at the current time.

Nevertheless, in the absence of a commitment to wholesale change, there are a number of approaches, initiatives and teacher research-led projects that can be implemented. These should be considered as confidence-raising exercises to develop awareness, experience and methodologies for the more extensive changes that inevitably lie ahead.

Section B concerns itself with these smaller-scale elements that a department, or even an individual teacher, can contemplate and introduce at an experimental level.

The quality of such experimentation will be improved if the exercise is developed with buy-in from the senior leadership team and to an agreed and developing experimental rationale.

That the experiment is developed with a commitment to share methodologies, progress and results with others might represent the beginnings of the action-research programme of the school. Action research is part of the process of scaling the reflective learning posture of individual teachers into a mechanism for wider and sustainable change among the whole staff. This is the essence of an incremental approach to change. It centres on the quality of pupil engagement and learning progress.

8. A CURRICULUM FOR THE FUTURE: RECONCILING EXCELLENCE WITH PERSONALISATION

Building the future: from education to learning

Considerations of new and effective assessment models discussed in Chapter 7 are a necessary, but not a sufficient, requirement for the curriculum of the future.

Any attempt to engage fully with an ipsative assessment model in which the pupil actively engages in selecting the time, pace, methods and format of their learning would inevitably come into conflict with existing learning structures.

The dominant pedagogy of teacher-led exposition, classrooms designed for 1:30 teacher–pupil ratios, the tyranny of the lesson bell that truncates learning sessions to an hour's duration (or less) and the suspicion of pupil IT devices probably precludes implementation of an ipsative assessment model.

We need to appreciate where such organisational structures came from and why their redundancy is hampering all pupils from learning effectively.

THE MYTHOLOGY OF CURRENT SCHOOL ORGANISATION AND WHY IT NEEDS REFORM

The structures of learning around which most schools are organised have remained unchanged since Victorian times. There are benches in Eton College that go back many generations before then and bear the names of generations of pupils. Despite their antiquity, they are still perfectly serviceable to support today's learning.

These structures are largely artefacts of an industrial model of 'batch' education in which it is assumed that children of the same age must, necessarily, be educated together. Presumably, the underlying philosophy is one that believes that every child matures at the same rate so that 'batch' teaching is perfectly rational. Every parent and teacher knows this is not the case, yet this remains the rationale for teaching pupils in age-related groups.

A further misconception, accepted as truth, relates to optimal class size. The traditional mantra suggests that class size should be constituted in the ratio of one teacher to 30 pupils. Schools are built around this ratio. Indeed when working with the Building Schools for the Future programme, one of the most depressing elements of the initial engagements with headteachers was that, in envisioning the total rebuild of their school, their concerns were very conservative. Generally, they wanted the classrooms all to be the same size, the corridors to be wider, and for them to be freed of the money pit of the habitually leaking flat roof by replacing them with pitched roofs.

The 1:30 ratio has no rational educational explanation to it. Despite it being ubiquitous, it does not have a research basis behind it. It came about because, in the scramble to provide universal primary education in Victorian times, there was a desperate need for teachers. When, inevitably, sufficient trained teachers could not be found, recruitment came from army veterans. Such veterans were used to working in squads and platoons and their experience of working in the 1:30 ratio determined the recognisable class size that endures today.

Presumably, this recruitment strategy was based on the same flawed logic that has recently seen efforts to recruit ex-service personnel into the classroom. I am not suggesting ex-military cannot make fine teachers. They possess a level of broad life experience that many teachers who have gone from school to university and back to the classroom do not possess. However, there is a sub-text here that ex-military, be they Victorian Crimean War or modern Afghanistan veterans, will impose a level of strict discipline in their classes, whatever the impact on the learning in their lessons.

Teacher professional associations have perpetuated this myth. Like the famous Dickensian character, they insist that class sizes should not increase beyond the 1:30 ratio. This mimics Mr Micawber's famous, and oft-quoted, recipe for happiness:

Annual income twenty pounds, annual expenditure nineteen pounds nineteen shillings and six pence, result happiness.
Annual income twenty pounds, annual expenditure twenty pounds and sixpence, result misery.

(Dickens, 1850)

This quote perfectly parodies the insistence on maintaining the 1:30 staffing ratio.

I am not arguing that there is not a finite number of pupils that can be taught adequately by an individual teacher. I am insisting if the individual needs of pupils are to be met adequately, then it is far fewer than 1:30. That is, unless there are fundamental changes in the way teachers approach lessons.

A major advantage of schools in the private sector is that, generally, class sizes are smaller and give the individual teacher more time to support pupils effectively.

CHANGING THE ROLE OF THE TEACHER TO ENABLE QUALITY ASSURANCE

School funding, being per pupil based, will always make the 1:30 class size part of the funding calculation. This inevitably means that the only way the teacher can meet the individual needs of all their pupils is by using their time in different ways in the classroom. This requires moves from teacher exposition, with pupils being passive recipients of learning, to formative and, ultimately, ipsative learning models when the focus of the teacher is working in a coaching model to support individual pupils.

This, in turn, means that the learning diet must include greater self-supported and extended learning assignments, of the project-based learning type around which educators in Finland are building their curriculum.

REORGANISING THE PATTERN OF THE SCHOOL YEAR TO SUPPORT LEARNING RETENTION

Similarly, the termly arrangement of the school year has no educational foundation. It is an amalgam of accommodating the ecclesiastical holidays of Christmas and Easter as the church had such an influence on the development and influence of early education. As Easter is a movable feast, dependent on the moon's cycle, it habitually means that the spring and summer terms' end and start dates, and therefore half-term dates, move every year for no educational reason or purpose (Henry, 2008).

Moreover, the long summer holidays are a vestige of an agrarian economy where children would be required to help out at harvest time. This is hardly a meaningful consideration in the twenty-first century. Indeed, educational research has suggested that the long summer break has a detrimental effect on a child's learning. This educational research usually comes to the conclusion that moving to a more equal five-term model with a shorter summer break would be beneficial to the learning of pupils (McCarney, 2015; Doherty, 2017).

If what happens within school terms presently does little to support disadvantaged pupils, research evidence suggests that the poorest are proportionately impacted more by the long summer break. Stewart et al (2018) pointed to poor pupils being doubly affected by the long break in learning and schooling. The main findings of the research illustrated that poor provision of appropriate childcare, limited access to enrichment activities, and food insecurity meant that disadvantaged pupils' health and well-being can suffer and their learning stagnate or decline.

Clearly, many aspects of the current educational set up produce a deeply dysfunctional impact on the effective learning of all pupils. This is particularly apparent in the specific learning experiences and outcomes of pupils from disadvantaged backgrounds. To remedy this situation will require radical re-evaluation and reconstruction of learning.

In effect, many sacred cows which have characterised education will need to be slaughtered on the altar of transforming the learning experience of pupils. Indeed, the term 'education' will seem increasingly redundant, as the process becomes less teacher-led and more pupil-driven.

We are shifting the focus away from the consideration of the 'industrial' educational process, replacing it with consideration of 'learning' effectiveness as experienced by every pupil. Personalisation of learning encompasses these changes.

In this new model, the core components of learning are not expressed in terms of subjects or content, but instead are expressed in pupil qualities. Such an inclusive model needs to be built on a clear understanding of the world the pupil of the future needs to live and thrive within.

Case study

FUTURE LEARNING MODELS: FOUNDATION PRINCIPLES AT THE RSA ACADEMY

While the above analysis deals with the principles of change, what of the practicalities? Can such an ambitious programme of change be achieved from the current regime?

I have practical experience of managing this ambitious transformation from my time at the RSA Academy in the West Midlands.

From October 2008 until April 2010 I was seconded from my work on the Building Schools for the Future programme to support the development of the Opening Minds curriculum model at the newly established RSA Academy in Tipton, West Midlands.

The Opening Minds curriculum had been developed as the result of collaborative work between the Royal Society of the Arts, Commerce and Manufacturing (RSA) and the Confederation of British Industry (CBI).

The brief was to address the common refrain that young people left school less than job ready. This required a new curriculum designed to ensure that their time in school extended the range of experiences and developed the attitudes and behaviours required in the world of work.

It quickly became apparent from detailed discussions about the issues associated with the existing curriculum, as outlined above, that redesign of the curriculum was insufficient and that fundamental principles needed to be addressed beyond the curriculum remit.

Transforming learning: transforming lives

Translating that work into the design and operation of a new school was the responsibility of Principal Mick Gernon, along with the former Chief Inspector of Her Majesty's School Inspectorate (HMI), Mike Tomlinson, as chair of governors.

By the time of my appointment as the person responsible for the transformation of learning through ICT in October 2008, the transformation had already been underway for 18 months. The RSA Academy replaced the former Willingsworth School. Much work had already been carried out in defining new operational procedures and priorities, the new assessment models being particularly important as they would be the rails on which the Opening Minds curriculum would travel to new learning destinations.

Much time and creative energy was invested in the new school building, which, in design, would reflect the learning models the new Opening Minds curriculum would promote. In the two years before the new building would be operational, the Opening Minds curriculum would be rolled out in the existing traditional 1950s-style school building. Despite the building's limitations, some quite extensive remodelling took place to embed some critical Opening Minds elements into the existing learning spaces. In particular, adjoining classrooms were knocked together to enable the distinctive large group learning model to be incorporated. This encompassed up to 120 pupils, their teachers and support staff for what would be considered more than two traditional lessons, and usually for a whole morning or afternoon.

Additionally, the format of the lessons used time and space in new ways. The assessment criteria for ipsative learning were developed. These even introduced a new language to enable peer assessment, which otherwise would have been too harsh. Without guidance, pupils can be the harshest critics of their own, and their friends', efforts. The focus was on positive ways of framing constructive criticism.

The terms 'what went well' (WWW) and 'even better if' (EBI) became standard descriptors for framing constructive criticism. A new term, 'don't do this' (DDT) became a format by which pupils could share mistakes they had made in their response to the assignment. Experimenting, trying new ideas and being able to recognise and even celebrate failure as a valuable, if intense, point of learning was critically important in ipsative assessment for both pupils and teachers.

Time management, individual research, problem-solving, teamwork and communication skills underpinned every session and represented a fair reflection of the project management skills that pupils would need to employ in their professional life beyond school.

Table 8.1 Delivering an Opening Minds session

OPENING MINDS DELIVERY SESSION: 3 HOURS		
ELEMENT	TIMING	TASK
INITIAL TEACHER EXPOSITION OF THE TASK	NO MORE THAN 5 MINUTES WITH 10 MINUTES ALLOWED FOR PUPIL CLARIFICATIONS	THE TASKS WERE CROSS-CURRICULAR IN NATURE AND WERE BUILT TO ENSURE THAT THE VITAL SKILLS OF EACH SUBJECT WERE DELIVERED IN A PROJECT-BASED THEME.
PUPIL TEAM DEFINITION OF TASK AND DELIVERY PLAN	15 MINUTES	PUPILS WORKED IN SMALL GROUPS WITH TEACHING STAFF ON HAND TO SUPPORT AND COACH AS REQUIRED.
TASK RESEARCH AND DEVELOPMENT OF SHORT PRESENTATION OF FINDINGS STAFF ACTED AS COACHES AND SPENT TIME DISCUSSING HOW PUPILS WERE LEARNING EFFECTIVELY AS INDIVIDUALS AND IN GROUPS THIS REPRESENTED *REFLECTION ON LEARNING* AND *REFLECTION IN LEARNING*	120 MINUTES	SMALL GROUPS RESEARCHED THE TOPIC AND DESIGNED A PRESENTATION IN A MULTIMEDIA FORMAT TO PRESENT THEIR FINDINGS IN A COHERENT WAY. THIS SESSION WAS HEAVILY SUPPORTED WITH LAPTOPS TO ENABLE TEAMS TO RESEARCH AND DEVELOP AN APPROPRIATE PRESENTATION.

OPENING MINDS DELIVERY SESSION: 3 HOURS		
ELEMENT	**TIMING**	**TASK**
PLENARY SESSION	25 MINUTES	PUPIL GROUPS PRESENTED THEIR RESPONSE TO THE INITIAL STIMULUS USING PAPER AND ICT BASED MATERIALS. THE ASSESSMENT MODEL INVOLVED PEER ASSESSMENT AROUND A VOCABULARY WHICH INCLUDED 'WHAT WENT WELL' (WWW) AND 'EVEN BETTER IF' (EBI) TO ENCOURAGE POSITIVE DEVELOPMENTAL COMMENTS.
TEACHER PLENARY	5 MINUTES	TEACHER RELATED THIS LESSON TO PREVIOUS AND FUTURE ASSIGNMENTS AND COMMENDED PARTICULARLY EFFECTIVE EXAMPLES OF INDIVIDUAL SKILLS AND ATTITUDES, OR GROUP WORKING WHICH RESULTED IN EFFECTIVE PRESENTATIONS.

Operational changes

Underpinning the development of the Opening Minds model were some profound changes to the way staff operated. First, the subject departmental model was abandoned for three faculties, or schools. One school comprised humanities and languages, one sciences, design and engineering and a third the creative arts and sport.

This brought teachers together in larger groupings to share planning and discuss assessment and progress on a daily basis.

Working in radically new ways was not always comfortable for staff, who sometimes wished to revert to the familiar, rather than embrace the new formats and demands. The senior leadership team had the advantage of having some development time before taking over at the school to develop the new models. Considerable time was spent revealing the new requirements to staff at a sustainable pace so that they transitioned to the new ways of learning.

Routes to return to old ways of working were dismantled. There was no central staffroom; staff were encouraged to spend non-teaching periods in purposeful, learning preparation rooms. These had refreshment-making facilities but were dominated by laptop points and workstations rather than comfortable chairs grouped in circles. Staff ate lunch with the pupils and brought them down for a breakfast break in the morning.

The new school day effectively extended from 8am to 4pm and this constituted almost 35 hours of curriculum time per week. This ensured that the new three-hour units of learning could be accommodated. It also meant that one period per week could be given over to an elective session where pupils could choose a programme that would last for the whole eight-week term.

A learning bonus: elective courses

I introduced a course on film-making using Photo Story and Moviemaker from the Microsoft Office suite. Other courses included sports coaching sessions, drama productions, artwork, the development of an allotment as a microbusiness and role-play gaming.

These courses reflected the interests of the teachers or the demands of pupils. As every teacher was deployed in these sessions, the pupil–teacher ratio was made favourable. For some activities, such as the drama production, there was multiple staffing so that a complete production from technical and scenery painting to costume production and rehearsals could be produced in the eight-week timeframe.

Freed from the content demands of the curriculum and able to develop new ideas ambitiously, these sessions were a great success for pupils and teachers alike. However, the new working patterns were exhausting at times and staff relished the two-week break between each of the five eight-week terms.

For new members of staff, who had just qualified, this revolution in priorities and work patterns was possibly easier than for more experienced members of staff. Knowing no different, new staff members adapted quickly to the innovative demands of working at the Academy.

Post-16 provision: Opening Minds and the International Baccalaureate

For post-16 provision, there was no existing or developing Opening Minds provision on the horizon. There was a determination at the Academy that, after developing the new provision progressively from Years 7 to 11, leaders did not want pupils to revert to old ways of working at A level.

The curriculum model that most closely aligned to elements of the Opening Minds model was the International Baccalaureate (IB). Consequently, the Academy invested heavily in this programme at post-16 and, in particular, in the promotion of the Theory of Knowledge

(TOK) element of the course. This encouraged learners to take an enquiry-based approach to the *how* of their learning. This developed an active approach to study skills and learning effectiveness that complemented Opening Minds.

Evaluation and external scrutiny

There were concerns, as at all schools, that the scope of innovation might be so radical as to confound Ofsted inspectors who might come to the conclusion that Opening Minds 'did not compute' with their expectations. However, this was not the case. The team of Ofsted inspectors proved themselves very catholic in regard to methodologies. Their focus was firmly on the effectiveness of provision and learning outcomes of the pupils and the robustness of the evidence base used to track and record learning. No doubt, having a former HM Chief Inspector on the governing body gave valuable insights into how a radically new assessment base could test and develop new skills, while providing secure and meaningful data for national accountability measures.

The plenary: mapping the future

The challenge of such future learning models seems overwhelming, so let us return to a simple learning technique to organise complex ideas into digestible and graphical formats. Virtuous circles, a method that generations of my pupils will associate with my teaching, will bring structure to the design process.

Essentially, within your school you have three elements to repurpose:

1. the first and most important is defining the pupil of the future;
2. the second is defining the teacher and teaching process of the future;
3. based on these two dimensions, the third element is defining the most appropriate curriculum content and delivery model to maximise the impact of learning for every pupil.

The case has been made in this book for moving to a quality assurance model and for abandoning the quality control model that grades a proportion of pupils for failure. This requires a clear understanding of what the future pupil requires in terms of their progress in school, and in their life beyond school.

This in turn requires dismantling the knowledge-based model of learning and replacing it with an inclusive model that looks at the attributes the pupil will need to display in learning. These can be itemised as follows (see Figure 8.1).

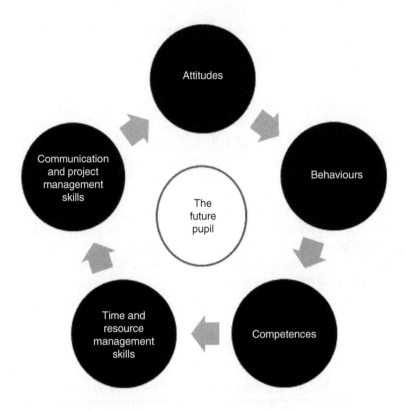

Figure 8.1 Defining the future pupil

ATTITUDES

These include the outlook pupils bring to learning tasks, such as motivation, positivity, a can-do philosophy, as well as the qualities currently gaining ground to overcome some educational concerns, such as mindfulness and emotional resilience.

Recognising that learning takes place in a variety of settings and groups means that the pupil must also develop the ability to be open-minded, fair, reasonable and non-discriminatory in their approach to others.

BEHAVIOURS

In order to ensure pupils do not begin any new learning task uncertain of how to proceed, learning must be more explicit in developing behaviours for effective learning. The ability to work independently, to interrogate and evaluate evidence and to be a self-starter who can work autonomously, asking appropriately for help and support, are critical behaviour skill sets.

COMPETENCES

This category encompasses many of the elements traditionally associated with subject teaching, but repurposed so that learning is seen as meaningful and coherent, rather than disjointed. Therefore literacy, numeracy and expression become cross-curricular aspects, rather than the exclusive preserve of individual departments. The example of the concept of 'evidence' that spans English, history, mathematics and the sciences is taught in a more unified way.

There will be new competences and new expressions of old competences such as interpersonal relationships, presenting to an audience, communicating in a range of formats and multidimensional research, which replace more standalone aspects of learning.

TIME AND RESOURCE MANAGEMENT SKILLS

In conversations with a number of NASA astronauts about future learning, I came across a common response. This was that the quality of the solution was always commensurate with how much time was available to conceive and implement it.

Astronaut Alvin Drew epitomised this aspect of project management when he said that the most vital question in any project was, 'How much time do we have?' That would determine whether a five-minute or a five-year solution was required. I thought these responses, from people who had explored the edge of the human experience, were so important they should comprise a key element of future learning.

Of course, this category would also include more earthly examples, such as financial education and effective time-management strategies.

COMMUNICATION AND OTHER PROJECT MANAGEMENT SKILLS

Having worked at the interface between education leaders, architects and building contractors, I would argue that every pupil would benefit from exposure to the sort of planning methodologies that builders employ. The ability to identify and reduce risk, to plan a path to a goal and to recognise the dependencies and priorities in workload management are skills for a successful life. Possessing the skills to build and sustain teams, within a family or in the workplace, provides a powerful platform for success and happiness.

This chapter has brought together a range of what appeared to be diverse aspects of the role of the teacher. It is only in Figure 8.2 below that these form a coherent picture.

Changing the assessment practice of the teacher is the starting point for development, because unless the direction and destination is recomputed, the teacher will not adopt new attitudes and ways of working in their daily role.

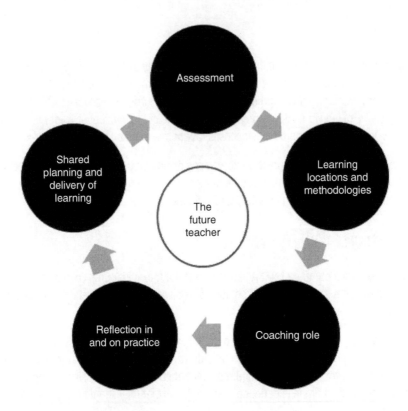

Figure 8.2 The teacher and teaching process of the future

Assessment protocols will allow for the re-evaluation of the 'where' and the 'how' of learning. This, in turn, will determine the role of the teacher progressing from knowledge provider to coach.

Thinking about what they do and the effectiveness of their practice and, critically, sharing that information freely with colleagues, are hallmarks of the effective future teacher. Only by reflection in and on practice, and a fully collegiate approach to improving learning, will the teacher become more effective. Reflection and collegiality are how the *event* of training becomes the *process* of continuous professional development (CPD).

CPD leading to sustainable improvements in pupils' learning can be enhanced further by the shared planning and delivery of the curriculum in teams.

When time is devoted to defining accurately what is required of the future pupil and teacher, a future curriculum becomes possible.

In the assessment element here, I am not simply referring to the formal assessment requirements of learning, but also to the profile of the future learner. Within the school, the pupil needs to focus on the key performance indicators that define the effective learner (see Figure 8.3).

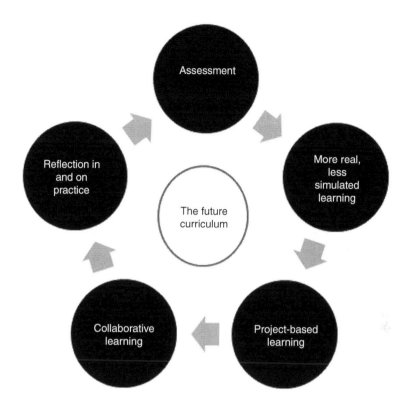

Figure 8.3 The curriculum delivery model of the future

The school needs to incentivise every pupil to continuously improve their performance in terms of punctuality, attendance, learning progress attainment, attitude and progress, service to the school and wider community and school environmental improvement as a minimum.

As well as these individual goals, the pupil should have substantive opportunities to develop their group working ethos, by class group, tutor group, year group and whole-school achievement benchmarks.

Securing this future curriculum will require support from the host community to ensure that learning is challenging, engaging and rooted in real-life experience. Furthermore, it should provide opportunities for individual and group project work from inception to realisation.

Summary

This chapter has brought together the content of previous chapters to consider some of the key questions of making your school fit to educate all your pupils for a successful future.

From key considerations about the shape of the future, we have isolated key components that are identified, not in terms of subject matter, but in new learning descriptors – attitudes, behaviours and competences. Conveniently, these spell out ABC.

Teachers will not be able to respond to the demands of the future until the drivers of their current behaviours are repurposed. Chief among these is assessment. Only when assessment priorities are addressed will teacher behaviours change to provide for new learning paradigms of the sort set out in principle, and in practice, in this chapter.

Further reading

THE OPENING MINDS CURRICULUM

The Opening Minds curriculum now informs the curriculum planning and delivery of a number of schools. Not all of them have the luxury of transitioning to the new model of learning in the comprehensive way that the RSA Academy enjoyed. Many are taking a more incremental approach to changing their curriculum offer to encompass new learning principles.

A full history of the development of the model, and implementation strategies, can be found at the RSA website: www.rsaopeningminds.org.uk/ (accessed 11 September 2019).

THE INTERNATIONAL BACCALAUREATE

The International Baccalaureate (IB) has been involved in the development of new learning approaches to improve pupil outcomes since 1968 and the programme has developed to encompass a complete curriculum from ages three to 18.

The primary focus on learner effectiveness characterises all the IB's work. The international nature of its work and support means that the best practice of many nations informs development of the curriculum.

Many teachers cite the Theory of Knowledge component of the course as being the most distinctive feature of the IB. This element encourages pupils to embark on their own research regarding learning effectiveness, around the principle that 'learning is learnable': www.ibo.org/ (accessed 11 September 2019).

Bibliography

Dickens, C (1850) *David Copperfield*. London: Bradbury & Evans.

Doherty, J (2017) *Why School Summer Holidays Are Too Long*. Leeds: Leeds Trinity University. [online] Available at: www.leedstrinity.ac.uk/blogs/why-school-summer-holidays-are-too-long-dr-jonathan-doherty (accessed 11 September 2019).

Henry, J (2008) Long School Holidays 'Are Bad for Children'. *The Telegraph*. [online] Available at: www.telegraph.co.uk/news/uknews/2023071/Long-school-holidays-are-bad-for-children.html (accessed 11 September 2019).

McCarney, M (2015) School Holidays Around the World: Do They Affect Pupil Performance? *The Telegraph*. [online] Available at: www.telegraph.co.uk/education/expateducation/11707907/School-holidays-around-the-world-do-they-affect-pupil-performance.html (accessed 11 September 2019).

Stewart, H, Watson, N and Campbell, M (2018) The Cost of School Holidays for Children from Low Income Families. [online] Available at: https://journals.sagepub.com/doi/full/10.1177/0907568218779130 (accessed 11 September 2019).

9. EBBINGHAUS AND THE FORGETTING CURVE: MASTERING ACQUISITION, RETENTION AND RECALL OF INFORMATION

Critical issues

» Without strategies to manage the acquisition, retention and recall of information, the tendency is for learning to be lost at an alarming rate.

» Schools tend not to address the issue of learning loss. The nature of the curriculum, being content-heavy, means that class learning can be very inefficient.

» Metacognition, the science of understanding how the brain works as a learning organ, is still in its infancy. Its findings are heavily nuanced and not necessarily in a form that schools can use practically to improve learning.

> » **Study skills are one approach to thinking through the 'how to' of learning that can be applied effectively across the whole school curriculum, but require a consistent approach to yield results.**
>
> » **The Ebbinghaus effect can be countered by the application of learning management techniques across the school.**

Ebbinghaus and learning retention

I did not feel particularly well prepared when starting my teaching career. Even so, of the myriad information about ideas and concepts I had yet to encounter, the work of Ebbinghaus was probably the worst gap in my understanding of the learning process.

Hermann Ebbinghaus published his seminal work on memory and information retention in 1885. It suggested that the ability of the brain to retain and recall information over time declined quite markedly. The work has been popularised as Ebbinghaus's forgetting curve (Shrestha, 2017).

If you are interested in effective learning, Ebbinghaus's work should inform your approach and methodologies. I claimed in the introduction how a false and dangerous assumption was made in school-based education that 'learning' and 'revision' were two completely different processes. Ebbinghaus's view is one way in which you can review and reform learning in your school by unifying the underlying principles you bring to learning design. In this way, all teachers will be applying the same principles, and pupils will receive a consistent learning experience.

In summary, what Ebbinghaus said was that all learning was effectively meaningless, unless consideration was given not only to accessing information, but also to methods for retaining it. This is because, although the brain can absorb great amounts of information initially, over time access to this information dissipates and becomes unreliable.

This should not surprise us. If we thought about every image our eyes see every second, if we retained that information in its totality then even the phenomenal capacity of our brains to hold information would be challenged.

In effect, the brain requires a filtering system to decide on information that needs to be retained in its entirety, and elements that can be deleted to ensure there is capacity available to store new information. Research suggests that this process of prioritising information takes place as we sleep. Some information is stored in short-term memory, other elements are retained in the long-term memory.

Part of this filtering of learning is the gradual degrading of information by the process we call forgetting. The most famous aspect of Ebbinghaus's work was the graph that became known as the 'forgetting curve', outlined above and in Figure 9.1.

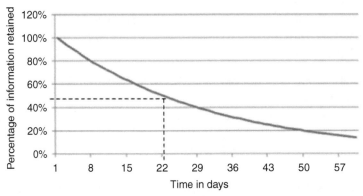

Anything learned would, over time, be lost to effective recall, or forgotten. In his test group he suggested that, on average, 50 per cent of information would be lost within three weeks.

Figure 9.1 The Ebbinghaus forgetting curve

Some people have what might be considered to be a better or even a 'photographic' memory. But these people are the exceptions to the general rule. There is evidence of people who are described as having 'autistic spectrum disorders', or who have received a brain trauma, who are able to have a memory function far in excess of the more representative subjects with whom Ebbinghaus worked. One of the most famous of these is Stephen Wiltshire, who can record vast amounts of detail from just a cursory view. He has become famous for his detailed views of buildings and cities drawn from memory (Wiltshire, 2016).

Such super abilities related to memory are the exception, and often come at some social cost to the people displaying them. The rest of us are clustered around the significant statistic that unless other methods are employed, approximately 50 per cent of learning will be forgotten within three weeks of acquisition.

This has significant implications in terms of learning effectiveness.

Ebbinghaus's work is critical to the three elements of learning effectiveness. These were outlined in Chapters 6 and 7 as:

- acquisition;
- retention;
- recall.

The fact that these are governed by general brain processes means that making a distinction between learning in lessons and the process of preparing for revision is false and unhelpful.

In every learning engagement, the process of thinking about how the information is to be acquired, retained and recalled is critically important. This applies to lesson planning and delivery, as well as to the testing of information recall which should be part of every learning cycle. The principles of revision should correspond to a similar learning cycle.

Metacognition: the science of how we learn

Ebbinghaus's work can be considered as one of the earliest recorded contributions to the science of how we learn. This area of study has developed into the research area called metacognition, which considers how the brain works as a learning organ.

There is particular interest in this area of study at present, and not just for school-based learning. The development of artificial intelligence (AI) is dependent on a clearer understanding of how the brain works, not just in control of bodily functions such as hand–eye co-ordination, but also in movement. There have been massive leaps forward in applications from this research in terms of robotics and miniaturisation. There have been vast expansions in the memory available to smaller devices.

However, metacognition researchers are only just beginning to tackle higher-order thinking skills related to memory function and operation. Issues such as moral choices, humour and metaphor present great challenges to research and defining what might be considered fundamental human qualities.

Translating scientific studies and medically based research into practical outcomes in schools is fraught with difficulties. Some of these issues were outlined in the 'magic bullet' solutions to learning improvement outlined in Chapter 4. Metacognitive research is incredibly nuanced, whereas teachers are looking for instantly applicable solutions. The result is that research findings are packaged inappropriately in a simplified form.

The outcome was an approach such as 'learning styles', which had teachers acting as diagnosticians, busy labelling pupils as 'visual', 'auditory' or 'kinaesthetic' learners. The pupils were then given badges and exercise books in appropriate colours so they could be identified and challenged appropriately in the classroom.

Teachers had identified particular pupil preferences that had developed as a response to the limited learning delivery models deployed in the classroom by the teacher. It was not the case that these indicated more fundamental preferences of the pupils when given a full range of learning options (Crooks, 1988).

When the limitations of this model began to emerge, the teachers reverted to their previous patterns of teaching; another attempt to systemise, codify and share effective practice having been discredited. The teachers therefore reverted to their subject siloes and little changed in learning.

Study skills approaches by the book

A more focused approach concerns the inculcation of study skills. These often do not engage with any metacognitive research and rely more on approaches that are seen to be 'tried and tested'. This is both their strength and their limitation, because they are often idiosyncratic and not introduced in a systematic and thoughtful way. Indeed, there is a considerable industry devoted to the development of study skills that, at worst, preys on the insecurities of teachers and parents alike.

The most simplistic, and most highly profitable to authors and publishers, are the subject revision guides that take up large shelf space in bookshops. These merely repackage the range of information required in the examinations into a slightly more digestible form. A full paragraph in your lesson notes is condensed into three bullet points. An essay plan is reduced to an A5 card of colour-coded keywords.

There is much merit in this approach. It has a very long pedigree as a technique through which to approach revision. Indeed, when I took my A level history examination in the 1970s, it came after two years of annotating the spoken notes of the history teacher's prize pupil from 1956. He had gone on to read history at Cambridge. The teacher declared that if it was good enough to see him through to such an esteemed institution, it was damn well good enough for us! It was the same history teacher who, when I said my interest was in twentieth-century modern history, declared that there was no such thing – that I was simply dallying with current affairs.

What is demonstrated in such revision guides is a useful technique. However, it is compromised by the fact that the essential elements of processing information into a condensed form, which has meaning when packaged and can be retained and recalled easily, is done for the reader by the author. If the books are used as templates for the individual pupil to go through the process of condensing information into a new format, then the technique is valid. If the pupil merely intends to passively read the condensed form of information of others in the hope of digesting it, then the process fails. In the latter case, information can be acquired, but will not be effectively retained or recalled because the Ebbinghaus forgetting curve will take its toll on poorly absorbed information.

The hard and fast rule here is that, although others can give guidance and sound advice about techniques, learning can only be achieved by the engagement of the individual in the process. For any study skill approach to work, the individual pupil must be convinced that it is a better option than their own traditional way of learning. Unless they can see for themselves the absolute benefits of a new technique, and this requires time and effort to do comparative tests of old and new techniques, there is a lot of inertia in the techniques deployed by both staff and pupils in a school setting (Elmore et al, 1996).

Overcoming the Ebbinghaus effect

Given the inertia of entrenched learning preferences with teachers and pupils, how can we introduce new learning methods? Accepting that up to 50 per cent of information acquired will be lost within three weeks, how can we decrease such losses?

The first, and most certain, path you can take is to respond to Ebbinghaus's research.

The degrading effect on learning put forward by Ebbinghaus can be offset by the use of particular techniques. These techniques generally require both overlearning of the learned content through repetition, and changing the length of time taken to study. These techniques work best when employed together as a systematic approach.

The starting point for this technique is to determine the most effective time period for learning. In terms of learning acquisition, this tends to be about 25 to 30 minutes, providing the stimulus is sufficiently engaging (Wikipedia, 2019a). Beyond this point, concentration tends to wander and learning efficiency declines. You can test yourself by reading and writing down information around a topic. There are times when the subject matter is so engaging that you can concentrate for much longer. However, in circumstances when you are learning independently, perhaps in a home or library environment, 30 minutes is perhaps the limit of your concentration. Indeed, for many, actually sitting down to start the learning process is the most difficult part of the process.

Psychologically, this is a very important finding. The idea that you only have to revise for a half-hour period, then take a rest, works wonders for motivation because it is possible. Revision is all about the art of the possible. Thirty minutes is a manageable timespan to work through. Once the target is manageable, it is achievable.

If you attempt to continue concentrating on learning acquisition beyond 30 minutes, then the efficiency of your learning degrades very quickly. Therefore, no more than 30 minutes should be the size of any learning period.

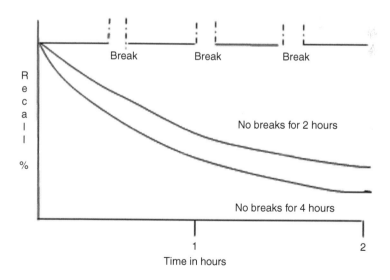

Figure 9.2 Effective acquisition, retention and recall of knowledge

Figure 9.2 stresses uniform, concentrated and short learning periods, punctuated by a break which is characterised by relaxation followed by re-engagement. This proactive approach maximises learning efficiency and effectiveness. Once the 30-minute timeframe is accepted, the second component is the process of learning or revision in that timeframe.

The critical element in all learning is to consider the brain as a computer. It requires information to be presented to it in a format that it can process.

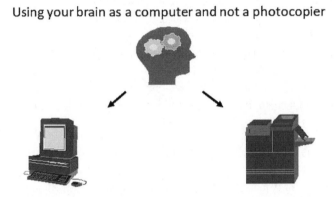

Using your brain as a computer and not a photocopier

Figure 9.3 The brain: photocopier or computer?

Unfortunately, left unguided, pupils tend to consider their brains to be photocopiers, capable of taking a mental picture of any information presented to them. Consequently, the first revision technique that pupils deploy is reading their notes or textbooks. They should be discouraged from doing this for two reasons.

1. First, words in paragraphs are almost indigestible as a means of acquiring and retaining knowledge.

2. Second, it would take as long to learn effectively in this format as it took to read the information in the first place.

Therefore, the general learning process and the particular relearning skills required for revision require active engagement and compression of information. Your pupils are not learning if they borrow the notes of others, or reread the textbook or your teacher notes.

To learn and revise effectively, pupils need to be compressing information into a format that the brain can process. This requires being inventive, and thinking more in diagrams and maps and less in plain text. Some specific ways of doing this are discussed in Chapter 10. Figure 9.3 is an example of such a compression technique in which many paragraphs of writing can be compressed into a simple diagram. However, is it as effective as it could be?

If, over a series of 30-minute sessions, pupils process information from their initial reading to the making of condensed ideas then they are giving their brain the best opportunities to digest the information in a form that will aid retention and recall.

Implementing the new learning technique in the classroom

The dominance of teacher exposition, and difficulties in securing quiet conditions in which to work intensively, make it more problematic to employ this technique in the standard classroom. To be successful, the learning diet of pupils should be more geared towards opportunities to learn independently, to consider information in greater depth and to have space and materials to map out their ideas.

Pupils would also need time to be introduced to the technique and the merits of its use in terms of efficiency of time and effectiveness of recall.

Picking up the idea of the ipsative assessment model discussed in Chapter 8, where the teacher acts more as a coach, this short-burst learning model mirrors the sporting metaphor introduced there. In athletics, this intensive activity, punctuated by a recovery activity, is known by the Swedish term, as 'fartleking,' or speed play (Wikipedia, 2019b). I can guarantee, that once this term is introduced to pupils preparing for revision, they will never forget it. Why this is so is explored in Chapter 10.

Projecting into the revision programme of pupils, Figure 9.4 shows how the fartlek process can be used to structure revision into short periods. An extra 15 minutes has been factored into the process to give time for the pupil to arrange their ideas and get focused on the intensive 30-minute revision.

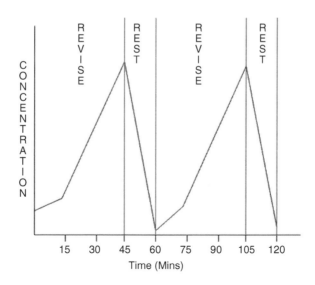

Figure 9.4 Overcoming Ebbinghaus: the fartlek approach

Working from this initial planning system the pupil can then build evening revision plans that factor in social and eating times. The suggestion would be that they use the last session of the evening to plan the following day's revision plan (see Table 9.1). The last session before bedtime should always be a relaxation period, otherwise they would take their revision to bed with them, with negative consequences for their ability to get to sleep.

Although this appears quite an onerous evening's revision, the combination of forward planning and the pupil never having to focus on more than half an hour's concentrated work at a time make the programme achievable. Four nights of this programme, at its most intense, gives the pupil Friday night off.

4.30–5.00	History	1	Plan a question
5.00–5.30	Maths	1	Plan a question
5.30–6.00	Tea		
6.00–6.30	History	2	Write your answer in a set time
6.30–7.00	Rest		
7.00–7.30	Maths	2	Write your answer in a set time
7.30–8.00	Coronation Street		
8.00–8.30	History	3	Check your answer
8.30–9.00	Maths	3	Check your answer
9.00–9.30	Rest		
9.30–10.00	Plan tomorrow's revision		
10.00–10.30	Relax		

Table 9.1 An evening revision plan

❖ Triangulation point

1. **Has consideration of the Ebbinghaus forgetting curve formed part of the lesson preparation programmes and revision strategies of your school?**

2. **Does your school revision programme go into sufficient detail about the *how* as well as the *what* of revising?**

3. **Who is responsible for planning and implementing the revision programme across the school? Do they have the resources available to ensure all pupils are well prepared by all departments?**

Summary

This chapter has explored one of the most important considerations in learning. This is the tendency of the brain to forget information which is not presented in a format that allows it to be processed, retained and recalled.

Although Ebbinghaus's forgetting curve is a well-known phenomenon, it is remembered only infrequently when teachers plan lessons, or when pupils embark on the solitary journey of revision. This means that, in lessons and revision, learning is sub-optimal.

Some initial techniques have been introduced here that adapt the athletics' term 'fartleking' to learning. This emphasises the need for short and intense learning sessions and for breaks in learning. The need to process information for learning into formats which the brain can acquire, retain and recall (ARR) has been introduced, to be developed in subsequent chapters.

Bibliography

Crooks, T (1988) The Impact of Classroom Evaluation Practices on Students. *The Review of Educational Research*, 58(4): 438–81.

Elmore, F, Peterson, L and McCarthey, S J (1996) *Restructuring in the Classroom: Teaching, Learning, and School Organization*. San Francisco: Jossey-Bass.

Shrestha, P (2017) Ebbinghaus Forgetting Curve. *Psychestudy*. [online] Available at: www.psychestudy.com/cognitive/memory/ebbinghaus-forgetting-curve (accessed 11 September 2019).

Wikipedia (2019a) Attention Span. [online] Available at: https://en.wikipedia.org/wiki/Attention_span (accessed 11 September 2019).

Wikipedia (2019b) Fartlek. [online] Available at: https://en.wikipedia.org/wiki/Fartlek (accessed 11 September 2019).

Wiltshire, S (2016) Autistic Artist Draws Mexico City Using Photographic Memory. [online] Available at: www.youtube.com/watch?v=ejhNxNIKvOI (accessed 11 September 2019).

10. PERSONALISING REVISION

Critical issues

» Bridging the gap between education and learning.

» Promoting the acquisition, retention and recall (ARR) of information.

» Personalising the learning process: patterns and sequences.

Education and learning: key distinctions for effective individual learners

Throughout this book, an implicit distinction has been made between the education process and the learning process. The differences between these two processes need to be made explicit when considering personalisation in more depth (see Table 10.1).

Many people use these two words, education and learning, as if they are the same thing. They are not, and understanding the difference between them will have a decisive impact on the effectiveness with which pupils develop the capacity to become successful learners.

- Education is a process through which society passes on knowledge and skills from one generation to another.
- Learning can be defined as the individual acquisition of new skills, knowledge, and values.

Both learning and education have a great influence on the mind and character of an individual. However, learning is the basic instinct possessed by all individuals, while education is acquired by individuals, usually in the formal setting of school.

Education is the process of imparting knowledge, values, skills and attitudes that can be beneficial to an individual or society.

Learning is the ability of the pupil to adapt this knowledge, through values and skills in a particular context, to analyse information, problem-solve and communicate coherently a solution in an appropriate format.

Learning is an ongoing process. An individual is always learning, from the moment of their first breath at birth (and indeed before this in the womb) until the last breath at death.

Education is something that one is given formally (it is usually compulsory) at some point in one's life.

Certainly, learning is an informal process. Education is a formal process, supervised by, and usually within, a school or college setting.

Education is something an individual receives from an outside source – predominantly, the school. Education is an extrinsic experience.

On the other hand, learning is something that evolves in the inner self and is the way we make sense of the world. Learning is intrinsic to the person.

Table 10.1 Differences between education and learning

EDUCATION	LEARNING
EDUCATION IS A PROCESS THROUGH WHICH A SOCIETY PASSES ON THE KNOWLEDGE AND SKILLS FROM ONE GENERATION TO ANOTHER.	LEARNING CAN BE DEFINED AS THE INDIVIDUAL ACQUIRING NEW SKILLS, KNOWLEDGE, AND VALUES.
EDUCATION IS ACQUIRED BY INDIVIDUALS USUALLY IN THE FORMAL SETTING OF THE SCHOOL.	LEARNING IS THE BASIC INSTINCT POSSESSED BY ALL INDIVIDUALS AND TAKES PLACE IN ANY SETTING.
EDUCATION IS THE PROCESS OF IMPARTING KNOWLEDGE, VALUES, SKILLS AND ATTITUDES, WHICH CAN BE BENEFICIAL TO AN INDIVIDUAL OR SOCIETY.	LEARNING IS THE PROCESS OF ADAPTING THESE KNOWLEDGE, VALUES AND SKILLS TO A PARTICULAR CONTEXT.
EDUCATION IS SOMETHING THAT ONE IS FORMALLY GIVEN (IT IS USUALLY COMPULSORY) AT SOME POINT IN A PERSON'S LIFE.	LEARNING IS AN ONGOING AND INFORMAL PROCESS, ENGAGED IN WHEN DESIRED BY THE INDIVIDUAL.
EDUCATION IS A FORMAL PROCESS, SUPERVISED BY, AND USUALLY WITHIN, A SCHOOL OR COLLEGE SETTING.	LEARNING IS SOMETHING THAT EVOLVES IN THE INNER SELF AND THE WAY WE MAKE SENSE OF THE WORLD.
EDUCATION IS SOMETHING THAT AN INDIVIDUAL GETS FROM AN OUTSIDE SOURCE - PREDOMINANTLY THE SCHOOL. EDUCATION IS AN EXTRINSIC EXPERIENCE.	LEARNING IS INTRINSIC TO THE PERSON.
EDUCATION IS ASSESSED AND VERIFIED BY AN EXTERNAL BODY.	THE UTILITY AND ASSESSMENT OF LEARNING TAKES PLACE INTERNAL TO THE INDIVIDUAL AND DERIVES FROM THE INTRINSIC VALUE AN INDIVIDUAL PLACES ON THE LEARNING EXPERIENCE
EDUCATION CAN BE MEASURED AGAINST VERIFIABLE STANDARDS.	LEARNING EVOLVES AT THE PERSONAL LEVEL, FOR WHICH THERE ARE NO SET STANDARDS.

This extensive preamble is important because when a pupil reaches the time of formal examinations at age 16, the formal structures of education fall away, leaving the pupil to fall back on their own personal learning attitudes and behaviours.

In an education system, inordinately built around information transmission, there are many startling assumptions made about the capacity of the individual pupil to respond effectively as an independent and autonomous learner in the run up to the examinations.

RE-EXAMINING SUCCESS

The more effective schools will have considered some of the requirements of developing the ability of pupils to learn independently in the period between the end of formal curriculum teaching and the start of the revision process.

The most effective schools will have built such ability to learn independently from first principles when the pupil entered the school in Year 7. Teachers will have developed these skills continuously throughout the pupil's time at the school. In such effective schools, the transition between class-based learning and revision is seamless because the pupil has the attitudes, behaviours and competences built and tested to survive as an independent learner. Additionally, each pupil will have developed considerable emotional resilience in order to withstand the pressures of preparation for and sitting examinations.

This chapter explores what the personalisation of learning requires in the examination preparation period. This allows schools to cross reference core ideas presented here against their current and future practice regarding personalising and codifying the curriculum to meet the needs of pupils.

Whereas Chapter 9 considered the time element of independent learning and discipline, this chapter considers how to process information for effective acquisition, retention and recall (ARR).

Managing information for ARR

The previous chapter considered the optimal length of the learning period, which was based on the mean concentration span of learners. This chapter explores what should fill these 30-minute learning units. It unwraps the effective learning processes in terms of a number of key techniques.

These key techniques for ARR can be summarised around themes.

The first technique is personalising learning so that the individual pupil can visualise and use trigger words. The second technique relates to patterning and sequencing. The third deals with overlearning, returning to previously learned information and perhaps applying a second learning method to strengthen command of the information.

PERSONALISATION OF LEARNING: TRIGGERING AND VISUALISATION

The most significant starting point for this exploration is a list of techniques that are least helpful in terms of learning effectiveness. These include the following.

- Reading notes

  Reading alone is a very ineffective way of applying ARR to learning. If the notes are the work of other people, the learning task is doubly complicated and information will be poorly acquired and retained. Even a pupil's own notes, which have been put together from a range of sources, will not be retained or recalled easily from this format. The problem is that notes alone are insufficiently condensed to aid the learning process.

- Annotated notes

  Annotated notes with headings, sub-headings and points and sub-points represent a marginal improvement on reading, because there is more a sense of order, importance and flow in their structure. However, they still do not package the required information in a format conducive to learning.

- Keywords and relationship diagrams

  In annotated notes, the structure of what goes into which level of importance is determined by the original longhand version of the text. In keyword and annotated notes, the pupil at least has the freedom to organise the information in a format and with relationships highlighted by their own understanding of the information. Specialised versions of relationship diagrams, such as mind maps, move closely to valid techniques for ARR.

The fundamental difference between effective and ineffective information acquisition techniques is associated with how much the individual pupil is able to arrange, prioritise and synthesise the information for the three elements of the ARR process.

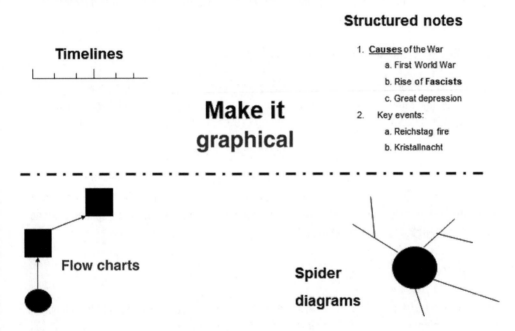

Figure 10.1 Techniques for managing information acquisition

The reduction in the amount of text and the use of relationship prompts to show both the priority and flow of the information greatly aid learning acquisition. Relying on the original written text, or on notes generated by others, does not allow the pupil to condense information in a meaningful way, which assists the ARR process. For this reason, techniques below the dotted line in Figure 10.1 will always be more effective than those above it.

The subtitle for this section is 'triggering' because effective learning techniques involve the development of a trigger word which then opens the subset of related words. Progressing to the next level allows the opening of the sub-subset of key words. The brain has only to deal with the limited amount of information held at each level, and this pattern follows a logical sequence.

In terms of retention and recall, this is the equivalent of holding information in a filing cabinet. If pupils know in which drawer the keyword is filed, they can open it and access the main headings or files associated with the keyword. Once the appropriate file is accessed, pupils can find the underlying data, stored in a meaningful order.

Visualisation of the learning process, as with the filing cabinet analogy, is very important to communicating such learning skills to pupils. We often witness a point where a pupil finally understands a new idea when they say 'I see it now!' This visualisation of the learning process is fundamental to the effective learning process and should be incorporated into teaching as often as possible.

PERSONALISATION OF LEARNING: PATTERNING AND SEQUENCING

Valuable as they are as techniques to support ARR, triggering and visualisation are necessary but not sufficient conditions to promote effective learning.

Patterning and sequencing play equally important parts in assisting effective learning through ARR.

Neuroscience is coming to a complex understanding of the way that information is acquired, stored and recalled in the brain.

The brain is powered, like a computer, by electrical impulses and information and memory reside in molecular level units called neurons. Neurons are connected together by synaptic connections. Consequently, the more synaptic connections linking the respective neurons, the stronger the ability to retain and recall information. In Figure 10.2 below neuron A has fewer synaptic connections than neuron B.

The ability to create new synaptic connections is called neuroplasticity. The brain can develop, or lose, synaptic connections over time. Learning is the process of generating new synaptic connections. Pathological illnesses, such as dementia, degrade these connections, leading to loss of memory, either short-term, long-term or both.

New information is acquired most effectively when it can be processed by the brain in a form that relates to existing knowledge sequences that were already stored. Alternatively, if it is processed in the form of patterns, rather than individual pieces of unrelated information, the brain will find it easier to acquire and retain. This accounts for the importance of triggering and visualisation and for patterning and sequencing.

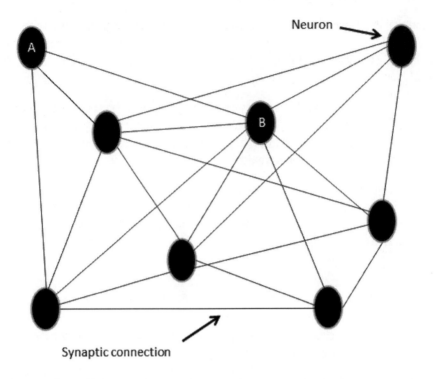

Figure 10.2 The learning brain: neurons, synapses, patterns and sequences

This learning process can be demonstrated in a simple way. Look at the information in Figure 10.3. Take no more than ten seconds to absorb it and then carry on reading.

Twelve words to absorb are well within the capacity of the brain. So remembering this information should not be too onerous. Now close this book and read something else for two minutes. Then, without reopening this book, write down, in the order presented, the 12 words.

Toyota	Blue
Seventeen	January
Sierra	Mondeo
Twelve	Thirty-six
Red	November
March	Yellow

Figure 10.3 Key words to learn

In fact, it will prove almost impossible to remember the 12 words. This is because they are provided without context; they do not form a pattern or a recognisable sequence. Consequently, they are merely 12 individual items to be remembered. This random list is difficult for your brain to acquire, retain and recall.

Such illustrations show how difficult it is to remember unprocessed information. It is why pupils and adults often find effective learning so difficult. They often conclude that they have poor memories, or are not good at learning.

Technically, we are born with a fully functioning memory. It is the failure to present our memory with information in a suitable format that lets us down. The exciting news is that effective learning is a function of appropriate learning methods, and methods can be learnt. It is therefore surprising that schools do not spend more time concentrating on honing the learning effectiveness of pupils, through study skills, rather than feeding them unprocessed information.

To demonstrate this we will revisit the words, but this time we will impose a structure on them. The structure is presented in Figure 10.4.

CARS	COLOURS	MONTHS	NUMBERS
Toyota	Blue	January	Twelve
Sierra	Yellow	March	Seventeen
Mondeo	Red	November	Thirty-six

Figure 10.4 Finding the patterns and sequences

In Figure 10.4, some preliminary sorting of the information has taken place. Four groups have emerged. Now, instead of 12 random items of information, there are only four headings to remember and each heading reveals only three items to remember. Suddenly, the task looks easier.

Beyond these four patterns of three words, there are further ways of sequencing the information for effective ARR.

Colours

The colour group relates to a pattern we already know – that of the primary colours. That means that an existing learnt pattern covers that group. So, simply remember these as the primary colours.

Numbers

When presented with numbers, the brain will always try to impose an existing pattern or sequence on them. Luckily, two of the three numbers correspond to a known pattern, that of the 12 times table, representing 1×12 and 3×12, or the six times table representing 2×6 and 6×6. Now the only number we need to consider is the exception, 17. This last number, 17, is one away from the six times table pattern.

Months

The determination of the brain to impose order and sequences on information must be resisted here. We learnt the calendar months in a specific order and, as these months break this order, they present difficulties for learning.

The technique required here is to find a more appropriate order which encompasses the information to be remembered. Therefore, look again at the information and find the underlying pattern. In this case begin, counterintuitively, with November, and impose the rule 'miss a month'. Then the sequence reduces to a single item and rule. In fact, finding an underlying sequence enables us to impose a rule, which would mean the length of a sequence does not matter. If you can remember the rule, you can remember the sequence.

Cars

The cars represent the most difficult group on which to impose a sequence, unless it mirrors the types of car you have owned, and thereby has specific meaning to you. The sequence may well be easier for people with a keen interest in cars to remember because learning engagement and interest is a keen promoter of memorable learning. They might be able to impose their existing knowledge, such as that two of the cars are Fords. This might give them leverage to acquire this grouping. Those with less interest in cars might default to the pattern of the alphabetical order of the names, but this is a less memorable learning format. People who have trouble remembering all 12 words will find the cars sequence most difficult.

IN MY HOUSE

There are variations on the theme of sequencing and patterning, which pupils might feel equally comfortable deploying.

One effective technique is called 'In my house'. This involves taking something with which you are intimately familiar, such as the plan of your home, and making associations between the rooms and the items to be remembered. This then forms a walk-through sequence for your memory.

The format works in the following way. 'Outside my house was parked a Blue Toyota. I walked to the front door and the *f* of *front* reminded me of two Ford cars, the Sierra and Mondeo...'

So well imprinted is the pattern of rooms, cupboards, nooks and crannies in your home that you can use it to store a large amount of information needed for the examinations.

Figure 10.5 underlines the importance of patterning and sequencing in the effective learning of items. It shows that the brain operates on the same principles as the computer. Information has to

Your brain: photocopier or computer?

- Read
- Stare at things
- Rely on memory

- Write
- Program
- Visualise

Figure 10.5 Patterning, sequencing and overlearning

be actively entered into it. The more we are able to visualise and program the information that is to be acquired, retained and recalled, the more effective the learning experience will be.

Unfortunately, left to their own devices, and without support, pupils will tend to persevere with less than optimal ways of learning, such as those listed in the left-hand column. In effect, they are using their brains as a photocopier, which is highly ineffective. Their subsequent failure will erode their confidence and convince them that they have a poor memory or are a poor learner. Neither conclusion is a good foundation for improvement.

The observant will realise that this diagram has been presented before in an earlier chapter. This is not accidental repetition on my part. It represents a technique called 'overlearning', when you return to a previously learnt item and refine it when you have wider contexts for understanding it, or when important information is added to your initial understanding.

Case study

THE REVISION TOUR: BUILDING FROM FIRST PRINCIPLES

The information presented in this chapter is derived from a presentation I used to give to schools on the more general theme of revision skills. The presentation was initially marketed in Nottinghamshire, but I ended up touring the country with it. I was pleasantly surprised that a series of ideas that I considered fundamental to effective study seemed so innovative to so many school leaders – so much so that I was retained year on year to give this presentation to groups of pupils in Years 11 and 13.

My greatest regret was that I was habitually engaged only between the months of January and May. Depressingly, at no time did senior school leaders take the hint that effective learning techniques had much wider applications in pupils' learning. They did not appreciate the importance of introducing them in the first months of the pupils' learning journey at their school rather than just the last.

When asking the pupils to learn the random list of words, I would always ask those pupils singled out by staff as the brightest in their year to try and remember the list. When they could not do it, I would show them the effective technique and ensure that those who struggled with learning stood up in front of the year group of their peers and successfully reeled off the 12 words without difficulty. Nothing is more likely to change perceptions and practice more than to succeed in a high-risk environment using a successful learning technique.

❖ Triangulation point

1. Within your own school what helps and what hinders the development of learning techniques such as those presented in this chapter?

2. When and where is the most appropriate time and space in your curriculum model to develop such ideas to improve ARR?

3. Does your teaching and learning policy address the issues relating to ARR and individual pupils?

4. Do departmental handbooks address the issue of ARR and pupil learning technique development?

Summary

It was not the intention of this chapter to provide a complete overview of learning and revision strategies. That is available elsewhere in a host of publications by more esteemed authors whose sole purpose is to research and present new works in this specific area.

The focus of this chapter was to filter some of the more significant elements of effective ARR and independent learning. These are presented to schools in a way that they can examine their own provision within the wider learning diet offered to pupils. Beyond this, they can focus on overlearning the techniques presented in the preparations they make to support pupils sitting the statutory examinations.

MIND MAPPING

Possibly the most recognisable technique for enhancing ARR is mind mapping. The technique of graphically representing and ordering information using freehand techniques to show priorities and relationships was pioneered, and is commercially associated with, Tony Buzan.

Completed mind maps resemble the images of neurons and synaptic connections discussed in this chapter. There is a particular discipline required to create an effective mind map. This involves a person making explicit their understanding of the relationship between elements of a topic. The process of recording these relationships and the emphasis and pathways between them gives meaning to the learning.

The technique is widely acclaimed because it frees people from linear note-making and forces them to spend time thinking about the relationships and dependencies between individual elements of a topic. As a technique, it demands discipline, concentration and engagement: www.mindmapping.com/ (accessed 11 September 2019).

STUDY SKILLS

Stella Cottrell may be considered the doyenne of study skills books. She published her first edition in 1999 and has been a prolific writer on the subject since then. Exploring her books will give an encyclopedic outline of the development of study skill techniques and applications. The link to her publishers will allow you to access all of her work: www.macmillanihe.com/page/study-skills/ (accessed 11 September 2019).

II. SOCIALISING LEARNING

THE EVOLUTION OF COLLABORATIVE LEARNING

Critical issues

» What we mean by socialising learning and the discipline required to develop it effectively.

» Exploring the link between socialising learning and the use of learning technologies.

» How to implement socialised learning and the lowest common denominator software required to achieve it.

» Developing sophistication: case studies.

Defining socialising in the context of learning

Given the context in which learning takes place in schools, and in the home environment, socialising might seem an unusual element to consider as part of the process. Indeed, it is. Making revision for examinations into a social activity rather than a solo, independent experience might be considered counterproductive.

The difficulty of making an initial commitment to sit in one space and to focus totally on the work in hand, is never enhanced by having others sharing that space. Instead, it increases exponentially the opportunities for distraction.

For revision to be effective, nothing can compare to a dedicated space, a specific time and a pupil focused fully on the task. However, much can be done to prevent the feeling of social isolation and to improve the effectiveness of the revision process by introducing some purposeful social interaction.

Psychologically, working independently, when it is not seen as a normal requirement of day-to-day learning, brings a host of difficulties, summarised as follows.

1. Overcoming inertia

    Chapters 9 and 10 explored the key features of effective learning in some detail. However, even with this information, the pupil is still up against huge difficulties to keep to the patterns set out there when left to their own devices. The requirement to sit still, with the paraphernalia of learning around you, and to focus on a work schedule, seems to compete with a thousand other, more enticing uses of the time.

    The longer-term goals of learning success seem too distant, and the vicarious pleasures of an online chat or a television programme irresistible. Indeed, the repetition of this pattern of independent learning, deferred for social gratification, often leaves the pupil feeling that there is now insufficient time left to complete the required work. This, in turn, produces a sense of foreboding and panic, which eats into confidence and makes a purposeful start to learning even more unlikely.

    I write this knowing I describe my own too-frequent experience of intense independent learning, at school, at university and in my professional life (and probably yours). I rationalised my study habits with the belief that I work best when under time pressure and that learning inertia had to be overtaken by some panic before I would work purposefully. I now wonder at the opportunities I missed for some startling educational performances by leaving myself insufficient time to ruminate and develop ideas and only having time to slog through the required work at a fast rate.

2. Managing space and learning time purposefully

   A minimum requirement of a personal space for learning is that all the required learning materials are to hand and are easily accessible. The full specification for what I term the home learning environment (HLE) is unpackaged when we consider parental input to successful learning outcomes in Chapter 14. However, learning in the home should be associated with a particular space that fulfils all the basic requirements of providing sufficient light, materials and incentive to stay in that space and focus on the half-hour learning timeframe ahead.

3. Sticking to the plan and doing the right things in a timely fashion

   Thereafter, it is as simple, and as difficult, as sticking to the plan developed towards the end of the revision work completed the previous evening. It is important to remember to factor into the process some pleasurable 30-minute social distractions.

   Being dedicated to fulfilling the requirements of the plan needs greater motivation than failing to fulfil it. Developing and maintaining the commitment to the plan, the discipline to tick off the scheduled sessions as fully complete, provides an immense sense of fulfilment. It maintains a sense of purpose which overcomes the normal rhythms of motivation and lethargy.

   Psychologically, this performance mentality again mirrors the coaching model related to ipsative assessment models. When pupils are already familiar with the personal responsibility to learn effectively and to look for continuous improvement in the school setting, they will find this discipline easier to apply at home, and in the world beyond school.

None of these three points has touched on the socialising of learning. They are essential preconditions that need to be in place before socialisation can be introduced.

Here, socialisation refers to the process of sharing approaches and methods to cross check and refine learning. These range from general approaches to the specifics of how a pupil might address a particular examination question.

In this context, the socialisation of learning is greatly aided by information technology.

LEARNING TECHNOLOGIES AND SOCIALISATION

In an earlier book, *Future-Proof Your School*, I lament the failure of information and communication technologies (ICT) to make a decisive impact on learning effectiveness. My analysis suggests a number of related reasons for this. The major criticism is that educational leaders invested in ICT kit based on the features sold them by vendors, rather than the benefits to learning. Consequently, there was no educational rationale for their use. Complicating things further, the dominant pedagogy in schools meant that, when used, the ICT kit and software merely reproduced, in a more efficient format, the same old lessons that teachers would have delivered previously through 'chalk and talk', with the pupils as passive consumers.

Despite these gloomy observations, we must recognise that the pupils who share our classrooms are children of the digital age. They have never known a time when ICT was not all-pervasive. They own personal devices that have more processing power than computers offered a decade ago and are at the heart of their social life.

To neglect this exceptional aspect of the life of our pupils is to miss an opportunity to engage and support their path to becoming independent learners.

So, the socialisation of learning I refer to involves taking the social aspects of pupils' devotion to ICT and purposefully coupling it to their learning development.

How to socialise the learning process for greater effectiveness

This needs to be an explicit process. While you may wish to attempt a number of initiatives to test what works with pupils, the direction of travel should always be towards whole-school approaches which are robust and consistent in promoting pupils' learning effectiveness.

This exploration of online learning must, of course, begin with a statutory warning about online security. There must be robust processes and methods in place to ensure the safety and security of all pupils and staff when working online.

The following sections give a range of examples of how pupils can collaborate in their learning either in the context of school, at home or in the more intense process of examination revision.

Although your school may possess a very sophisticated online presence, delivered by a virtual learning environment (VLE), a managed learning environment (MLE) or a learning platform/portal (LP), the potential of such learning technologies does not concern us here. This is because, if we want to develop ideas that are universally applicable, we need to keep things simple. We cannot make assumptions that all pupils will have access to the appropriate kit, at a time and place of their choosing.

The examples outlined below explore the underlying principles of socialised learning. They deliberately take as their starting point the lowest common denominator of available software which will be universally available in schools and in public spaces like libraries (the value of which should not be underestimated). You may feel that you can move forward the principles outlined here onto more sophisticated pieces of kit or software. However, every step up in sophistication in the program used is accompanied by increasing demands on the kit available to pupils. It also compromises the requirement for these approaches to be universally available.

If your pupils can access these programmes through your online learning platform, then so much the better. They will be operating in what is, in effect, a secure walled garden, only accessible to authorised users and in which people can be held personally accountable for their actions.

However, we are assuming that all your pupils need access to these simplest elements of kit, ideally at home.

The following examples show how particular items of kit may be used to socialise learning in universally applicable ways.

Case study 1

MICROSOFT PHOTO STORY

It might seem particularly perverse to begin the case studies of the socialisation of learning by outlining a piece of kit which Microsoft no longer supports in its Office suite.

The cost of computer site licences might mean that you are still running earlier versions of Microsoft software and can access this magnificent program, buried deep in the Office software. If you cannot access it, you can make similar online assets using Microsoft Movie Maker, which is again available with any version of Microsoft Office. However, Movie Maker is more complicated than the wonderfully simple Photo Story.

Why Photo Story works as a learning asset

Photo Story compiles images, text, narration voiceovers, animations and a soundtrack in order to produce a multimedia asset. The asset is in the form of a series of slides with accompanying animated text, a spoken narration and, if desired, a soundtrack that could be compiled by choosing appropriate music in terms of pace and mood to accompany the images.

Learning scaffolding

In short, Photo Story was the simplest way of storyboarding an idea from conception to production. When the project was compiled to the creator's satisfaction, it was saved as a final film that could be shared, or stored, in a library of assets.

If we remove the word 'storyboarding' from the above sentence and replace it with 'learning scaffolding', the potential of Photo Story for the independent learner is revealed.

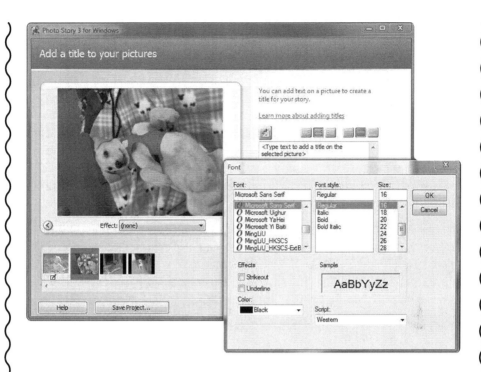

Figure 11.1 Scaffolding learning using Microsoft Photo Story

Used with permission from Microsoft

Motivation and engagement

The pupil is invited to engage in a creative process which is fun and enticing. This addresses the problem of getting the pupil to sit and overcome the standard objections to engagement in learning. Motivation is consistently high when creating a film, and the need to move carefully through stages to a final product maintains that interest to the end of the process (see Figure 11.1).

A finished film asset can be made within the 30-minute time limit that we set as an effective study period. However, such is pupils' engagement with the software, it is perfectly possible to maintain engagement over more complex projects, extending to several hours. I have used Photo Story as my learning asset of choice in learning projects with teachers, pupils in primary and secondary schools and adults with profound learning disabilities who had never experienced working with computers. Learner motivation was never an issue, even when the process extended over eight weeks.

Learning reflection and self-assessment

Moreover, the key thing we need to inculcate in independent learners, the ability to self-correct and assess the impact of their own work, is now made an internal and simple process. Previously, these elements were usually accomplished through the external process of teachers' marking. At any time, the pupil can move back a stage in the film composition and re-edit their ideas to make them more effective. This facilitates ipsative assessment in that the pupil can focus on improving their previous best effort independently. Pupils can even apply the process of peer review embodied in the evaluative term 'even better if' (EBI) to make improvements to their ideas in the course of the production process and before they commit to the final product.

During the editing process, pupils are required to marshal their ideas into a form that is easy for an audience to digest. To achieve this, they must deploy sophisticated higher-order thinking skills, displaying empathy and considering the requirements of their audience in terms of sophistication and engagement. In matching music and narration to images and text, pupils must consider the mood-setting and consistency of their message.

Case study 2

MICROSOFT WORD

The function I describe below is one that teachers may use in their everyday work. It was a regular feature of my work in senior leadership teams when documents were finessed through numerous versions to a finished product, each version being annotated and revised. I refer, of course, to the editing function in Word which is revealed behind the review button in Word. Given the power of this tool to work collaboratively towards a quality product, I am amazed it is not used more widely by pupils to mark and evaluate their own work and that of their peers. The incessant, time-consuming and inefficient commitment to written marking shown by school leaders and teachers is of particular interest in view of current concerns about teachers' workloads. This editing facility would appear to be a simple solution to reduce teachers' workloads. I have yet to see a school using this function of Word to promote self-and-peer analysis.

Peer marking in Word

Pupil work submitted in Word

Mark scheme

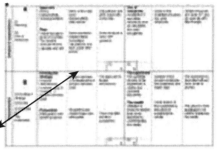

2. Mark scheme reference copied and pasted into comment section of document. Pupil can also free text write here.

1. The mark scheme document is open to allow you to copy and paste references to the pupil work.

Figure 11.2 Microsoft Word as a peer marking tool

Used with permission from Microsoft

In wishing to move from summative marking, characterised by pupils matching their efforts to an external, and often unshared, series of assessment criteria, to formative marking, where the marking criteria are known, I used Word to encourage pupils to undertake self-review and peer-review against the mark scheme (see Figure 11.2).

A simple series of colour-coded comments enabled pupils to tone their comments to be positive and developmental. This meant that pupils could deploy the key assessment language of 'what went well' (WWW), 'even better if' (EBI) and 'don't do this' (DDT), as well as indicating where they believed their peer had met the particular level of the mark criteria.

These marking exercises meant that the pupils became more intimately familiar with key criteria the examination markers were looking for, from the point of view of both the writer and the examiner. They learnt how to answer questions more effectively.

Case study 3

MICROSOFT POWERPOINT

There has been a feeling that Microsoft PowerPoint has been 'done to death' in schools. It was seen as the universal panacea for presentations and a byword for boring information transmission by bullet point, termed 'death by PowerPoint'.

The major drawback of PowerPoint was that it was so flexible as a communication tool that, in an effort to make the presentations more engaging, there was a tendency to prioritise style over content. The simplicity of operation also encouraged visual flamboyance, with titles and text flying randomly around, in what appeared to be an invitation to an electronically induced migraine.

The ability to present information in such graphic formats also had another, unintended, implication. It stopped people editing their work to a reasonable length that was precise and appropriate to audience. 'One more slide, one more animation', became the downfall of many a presentation.

My son epitomised this approach over a decade ago when he came home with instructions to complete a project on the Second World War. As a history teacher, with a particular interest in this period, I was keen to help him frame his thoughts and focus on a particular theatre of operations or campaign. My efforts to help were politely rebuffed.

'Dad, I don't need your help. I can get all the information I need off Google – pictures, words, maps and diagrams. All I need to know is whether the teacher wants a 100 gram or a one-kilo project!'

His comments epitomised a failure of education to embrace purposefully educational technology.

It was being used as an efficiency tool without making any contribution to the quality of learning engaged in by the pupil. There was no interrogation of sources or critical thinking. A beautiful, professional, heavy printed and bound document would land on the teacher's desk to great acclaim. At no point had the pupil experienced any learning other than compiling skills using PowerPoint and printing, using his father's good quality paper! Indeed, my son was commended on his well-presented and elaborate work, without comment on the 'copy and paste' mentality that had generated it.

PowerPoint and collaboration

I developed this approach to the use of PowerPoint when working with a school in Nottinghamshire. They were looking to use their suite of school-based and online resources to encourage their pupils to improve their revision and examination performances.

Like countless schools, they granted study leave before the examinations. Pupils were presented with a printed document with past examination questions and techniques for successfully answering them.

This was a tremendous conceit.

The teachers could say, hand on heart, that they had provided the pupils with the best advice to support their revision. The pupils could say that they had received this subject revision bible and would use it as part of their preparation. Both knew that the document would end up unused and, eventually, confined to the bin. Poor examination preparation was condemning most pupils to underperformance in the examinations and to limited horizons beyond.

The hidden benefits of PowerPoint as a learning tool

During discussions, we focused on using PowerPoint as the basis of a new approach to revision. It had the benefits of being familiar to pupils, and was generally liked for its speed and the impact it could make. Like all pupils, many had gone to the deepest recesses of the software and had found obscure ways in which to customise their work.

PPT: how to insert images

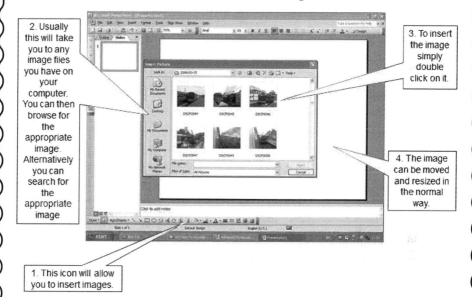

Figure 11.3 Microsoft PowerPoint as a revision aid

Used with permission from Microsoft

To this extent, PowerPoint was universally accessible and still held interest for the pupils. This was a critical factor because they considered work completed on the software to be creative and not 'real work'; certainly, not the tedious process of revision. Psychologically, the software got over the first hurdle of engaging pupils in the revision process (see Figure 11.3).

The fact that the school had a learning platform with secure pupil areas obviated the security issues of sharing information online. Each pupil could post to the departmental area where a folder was set up for revision presentations.

The most significant step in setting up the new process was an unusual one. In preparing revision PowerPoint slides for sharing in a library, there were some restrictions.

1. All presentations were to be reduced to a maximum of seven slides.
   This prevented the presentations turning into a 'tell me everything you know about a particular topic' format of the sort never asked in an examination.

2. The first slide in the presentation was to be formatted as a question to be addressed, and the last slide was to be a conclusion related specifically to that question. The questions related to past examination questions and there were even assessment criteria available to allow pupils to show how their answer met the criteria.

3. To address the issue of plagiarism associated with online sharing, all work completed by the pupils was published under the Creative Commons Licensing Arrangement. This meant they had to acknowledge where they had taken the work of other pupils and amended and developed it. An original piece of work would be tagged Version 1.0, with the name of the original author. A pupil using this work to produce their own version would label this as 1.1 and the original author credited. Subsequent pupils labelled their editions 1.2, 1.3 and so on.

4. Having placed all the previous revision notes in the online library, the teachers now invited the pupils to post their work there. However, the pupils needed to make a commitment before they had full access to this valuable and growing resource. To have full access to the online library, they had to submit, have moderated and approved by a teacher, three presentations before the library was open to them.

Using these simple guidelines, in the year of introduction, the department made a massive improvement in pupils' examination grades, almost doubling the five A–C grades obtained and better reflecting the full pupil ability in the grade return.

Pupil feedback

The pupils mentioned the greater incentive to sit and study afforded by doing work using a technology they enjoyed: 'It didn't feel like boring revision!' was a common strand of the feedback.

Having other work to read and analyse meant that they were not looking at a blank sheet, with no idea how to start to revise. This proved a great psychological boost.

The pupils appreciated that revision was an active process of engagement, and that merely reading notes generated by others would not secure an improvement in results.

A particularly interesting strand in feedback was that the pupils appreciated the particular demands of writing for an audience of their peers. This had made them focus on clarity of expression and grammar in ways that they would not have done if the work had been for purely for personal consumption, or was for the teacher to mark.

RE-EXAMINING SUCCESS

The pupils also appreciated the fact that their peers had found value in their work, and had developed their ideas into new and even better formats available to all.

However, despite the success of the project and the fact that it had been accomplished as an online exercise with home access, the delighted teachers did not make the connection with the process and begin to implement such strategies in the classroom. Here the diet offered to pupils continued to be dominated by teacher exposition.

Case study 4

COMIC LIFE

A non-Microsoft product that has a similar, if more linear, system of operation is Comic Life, available for a small licence fee.

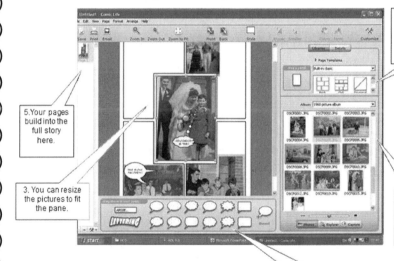

Drag and drop Comic Life page

1. You choose a page template here and drag it over the edit pane.

5. Your pages build into the full story here.

3. You can resize the pictures to fit the pane.

2. You select your pictures by browsing and dragging and dropping.

4. Speech bubbles allow you to tell your story.

Figure 11.4 Comic Life as a scaffolding tool

Used with permission: Comic Life by plasq.com

This allows pupils to scaffold their ideas into a comic book format. It is very simple to compile ideas, but is limited to the comic format for presentation. Perhaps this is better suited to particular subjects, such as plots and quotes in English literature. Pupils certainly enjoy working with it though (see Figure 11.4).

1. Given the particular mix of computer-based assets your school utilises, what impact do they have on pupils' engagement and learning outcomes?

2. Which applications of online learning and collaboration would you highlight as a strength in your school, and where do you see weaknesses in implementation and impact?

3. Are there particular needs for teachers' continuous professional development (CPD) that should be put in place to broaden and deepen collaborative learning in your school? What would be your priorities?

Summary

This chapter has concentrated on an aspect of learning that is often seen to be an anathema to learning in a school-based context: collaboration. Much of the way that schools organise the delivery of learning precludes and discourages this, partly because the end point of learning, the public examination, is a solitary test of the learning of the individual pupil.

In school, and beyond school hours, collaborations are intimately associated with new learning technologies, software and hardware. The examples shown here demonstrate how the technology must follow the learning need by giving the pupil the opportunity to slow down and effectively consider each stage in the development of their learning asset.

Building new and personalised ways to engage pupils is best constructed on a firm foundation of the simplest and most widely available software. The greater the specialisation of software, the less impact collaboration and online learning will have on learning standards.

The term 'socialising learning' has been used in this chapter to unify the twin topics of pupil collaborations, and the use of ICT to promote broader and deeper independent learning by pupils.

further reading

CREATIVE COMMONS LICENSING

The creative commons licensing is an attempt of copyright to catch up with developments in information technology. Since Web 2.0 became embedded over a decade ago, social media has allowed individuals to become not just consumers of online information but also producers.

As with the record industry, there have been great concerns that people were often writing in breach of copyright.

Creative commons is an attempt to redress the balance by allowing information to be used and repurposed, without breaching copyright as long as the original source is acknowledged. This is particularly important in an educational context where teachers are often looking to repurpose online images and writing to fit the learning needs of their pupils.

However, understanding copyright is also fostered for pupils by acknowledging the work of others when they share and repurpose online images, writing and other assets.

The hard border on creative commons is fair use that does not extend to commercial gain from the use of the work of others: https://creativecommons.org/licenses/ (accessed 11 September 2019).

COMIC LIFE

Comic Life is a storyboarding piece of software created in a variety of templates that mirror different comic book styles.

Images and text can be placed within the template frames to produce a stylised story. I found it useful as a way of encouraging pupils to edit down complicated ideas into the limited number of frames available.

When some vandalism occurred at a school in which I was teaching, I made the culprits write a comic explaining why their actions were selfish and potentially dangerous. They used their own mobile phones to take the appropriate images to build their story, and worked as a production crew to develop the story. It ended up being a particularly focused and powerful piece of considered work about actions and consequences. The final product could be printed and displayed, as well as shared electronically to inform others.

A negative experience was thereby turned into a shared learning experience which served as a warning to other pupils about vandalism: https://plasq.com/ (accessed 11 September 2019).

12. PARTNERS IN EXCELLENCE: THE SCHOOL IN THE COMMUNITY

Critical issues

» The isolation of the school from the wider community.

» The school curriculum and indifference to enterprise.

» Why things need to change in school community relationships.

» Vocational and academic learning: tackling the issue of parity of esteem.

» Modelling learning excellence in the community.

» The woeful state of careers guidance and work placements.

» Developing the community in the curriculum.

The monastic school

Although they are not, many schools behave in their communities as if they are a worthy charity. They approach engagement with their local community as if they were a well-loved local church appealing for support to make repairs to the church roof. The headteacher is almost apologetic in appealing for the time of local businesses or, even worse, for funding to ensure basic provision, or to get a new initiative off the ground.

Invitations for the local community to come in and see the school at work are strictly managed. The public relations aspects of such days are controlled to show the school in the best light. This suggests that the school is managing diminished budgets well and coping well.

It is quite possible to attend an open day or other event at the school, and come to the conclusion that what happens in the school is completely divorced from what happens in the local community. The school is a place of learning which is as grounded in the community as medieval monasteries were in their communities.

The difficulties of managing schools in times of reduced material support and greater performance expectations are glossed over in an attempt to show a successful and well-led organisation at work.

Engagements with local businesses are often telling. They approximate frequently to Oliver's interaction with the Bumble: 'Please sir, I want some more.' The 'some more' might be in the form of a direct appeal for money to maintain the existing curriculum provision, or even to complete basic maintenance work, rather than exciting new building projects or a curriculum initiative. It might be a one-way and one-time appeal to provide a work experience for a pupil towards the end of their formal education. These are engagements in the form of a single event, rather than an invitation for an extended process and ongoing relationship.

Such schools often fritter a disproportionate amount of the valuable creative time of teachers and support staff on procedural affairs. The most expensive of these cultural peccadillos includes maintaining a steely grip on the issue of uniform. The rationale behind this focus on what is not a primary element of learning in the school is based on Rudy Giuliani's philosophy of combatting crime in New York when he was mayor: if you focus on the little things, and adopt a zero tolerance of them, then they do not escalate to become major disciplinary issues.

Indeed, I have been amazed that in the set-up of new academies, an enormous amount of consideration has been placed not on discussion of the purposes and processes of learning, or the focus on inclusion and how it was going to be achieved, but on discussions of the new school uniform. If the school engaged in extensive discussions about the curriculum, excellence and inclusion with the same drive and determination as on uniform, then all pupils would receive a better education.

I characterise schools whose leadership teams display this attitude, in which they acknowledge that they are in but not essentially part of their local communities, as monastic schools. They behave as if what happens within the school organisation has no direct relationship with the economic well-being and cultural growth of the local community.

There are too many monastic schools. This is because the nature of educational leadership is determined by many teachers moving from the classroom, as pupils, to university and then straight back to the classroom. They have not experienced the wonderful potential and substantial difficulties under which the small and medium-sized enterprises that dominate their local economy operate. They have never had to steer a course between threats and opportunities using their strengths and ameliorating their weaknesses.

Surprisingly, given the separate orbits of school, industry and enterprise, every one of these concerning situations is staffed, and was started, by someone who went through the education system. Every business is totally dependent on the output of the school system for its future success.

Everything you would want in an independent and autonomous learner, negotiating their path through a changing world, is displayed every day by the best of local business. Yet many schools keep them at arm's length. They take a short-sighted view that they will appeal for money and resources from them to maintain the school on a parallel path in which learning is not contaminated by commercial or industrial reality.

This also means that the learning diet of the pupils is heavily based on simulation, rather than the application of attitudes, behaviours and competences for solving 'real-world' problems.

Enterprise indifference

Nor is industry beyond criticism in the field of fostering collaborations that give pupils real-world experience of operating in a commercial or industrial setting.

The largest of national and international employers do recognise their responsibilities to their host and, sometimes, their national community. Many now have a department devoted to corporate and social responsibility (CSR). This department liaises with community-based organisations and is often prepared to give seed-corn sponsorship to worthy local groups, of which schools are included.

The problem with sponsorship is that it is often expressed as a one-off payment, rather than a strategic relationship. It is directed at a short-term need and not a long-term project. Companies tend to eschew long-term relationships for fear of committing themselves to projects, over which they have no control, other than funding. The only management decision left open to them in such projects is to withdraw funding. So instead, they choose to spread their money exceptionally thinly, and across as many disparate projects as the community is pursuing.

The large company, and often small ones too, are content to have positive and regular popular press coverage for their efforts. As a result, the local school will have, for example, a school football kit supplied with the name of the local employer emblazoned on it. Both parties are seemingly content with this superficial relationship.

Small and medium-sized enterprises might take a similar posture regarding their relationship with local schools. Often the coffers for support can be extended if an entrepreneur attended a local school, or has children there. This might make them more receptive to requests for support, and more willing to support the school over an extended period, at least while their children still attend.

The company as a beneficial supplier, and the school as the grateful recipient of charity, defines the nature of this relationship.

Common ground and an existential need for deep collaboration

The nature of the relationship between industry, in all its forms, and schools needs to change radically and for the benefit of both parties. Ideally, this would be part of a national debate. Even without this, there are organisations in place that could promote it regionally. There are also forward-looking senior leadership teams, like those during my time at the RSA Academy, who have the tenacity to pursue local collaboration in the absence of a wider scheme.

Instead of the monastic tradition in schools, and the benign altruism of industry, the relationship needs to be reframed decisively. The relationship between school and industry is not parasitic, with the schools looking to tap the local employer for regular monetary contributions, but symbiotic, with both parties relying on each other.

The relationship is even deeper than this. Without effective schools preparing pupils who are independent and autonomous problem-solvers and lifelong learners, industry will not have the next generation of employees and entrepreneurs to drive future prosperity. The relationship between schools and industry is therefore an existential one and it is time both parties began to engage and collaborate on a broader and deeper scale to quality assure the learning of the next generation as being fit for purpose in the twenty-first century.

From industry, we need to hear less moaning about school leavers entering the job market without job-ready skills. From schools, we need to see behaviour that suggests learning has practical outcomes in the employability and future well-being of their pupils (Cassidy, 2014).

The future mission of the school should not be part of a quality control mechanism designed to whittle away pupils until only those judged capable of going to university are left. This unchallenged academic rationale for education is outmoded and deeply corrosive of the potential of pupils and, therefore, of community prosperity.

Vocational and academic learning: parity of esteem

Essentially, the radical change of direction in the purpose of schools must address the lamentable failure of British schools generally, and English schools in particular, to service vocational pathways. It has always been the case that more young people will enter employment through a vocational pathway than through the university route. Indeed, until recent expansions in the aspiration to go to university, the academic route had an alluring appeal because entrance was so restrictive (Hillage, 2018).

I do not decry that aspiration, but we need to urgently address the perception of the poor second option that vocational pathways are seen to supply (Dalby, 2015). We see this in constant tampering with vocational qualifications. It is reflected in the failure of apprenticeship schemes to supply sufficient technician-level young people to service the sunrise elements of the economy. All this is exacerbated by the constant underfunding, or inappropriate funding, of the vocational education route (*Guardian* Letters, 2019).

In England this woeful situation has manifested itself in three levels of crisis.

1. It has seen funding crises in colleges of further education, where lecturers are made redundant at the same time as there are recognised skills shortages in their area of expertise (Cope, 2018).

2. Small employers have been unable to grow or even maintain themselves because the financial and administrative costs of taking on, and training, an apprentice have escalated. They are therefore unable, and unwilling, to take on the financial burden of supporting apprentices, even though this lack threatens their future viability.

3. Exploiting this failure of the traditional pathways to supply sufficient technically qualified people, independent training companies have taken on contracts and then failed to complete the vocational training of young learners, declaring themselves insolvent in the process (Speckesser and Sala, 2015). This has been a long-term problem (Finegold and Soskice, 1988).

These systemic failures cannot be solved without a radical manifesto of change. This will involve major cultural shifts in those who provide education and those in industry who benefit from a skilled and adaptable workforce. The first requirement will be recognition of a parity of esteem, of the sort much vaunted in Germany, between academic and vocational learning pathways.

Excellence in the community: the school as engine of change and aspiration

A second requirement is a fundamental change of the learning culture in schools. This will provide, for all learners, a curriculum of excellence. Such a curriculum is quality-assured and personalised and gives the individual pupil sufficient resource, support and opportunities to be an active player in the economy and community of the future.

The school that is genuinely committed to excellence must have a rationale for community engagement. This appreciates that the school needs a process of osmosis between itself, its aspirations and resources, and those of the local community.

Schools can no longer act in the monastic tradition; their supine approach to industry for extra funding must stop. As Clement Attlee declared on the foundation of the welfare state: '*Charity is a cold grey loveless thing. If a rich man wants to help the poor, he should pay his taxes gladly, not dole out money at a whim.*' This maxim should apply to the relationship between schools and industry. Industry should not support schools vicariously, but rather as part of a national development strategy. Such a strategy would be geared to the needs and challenges of a future economy, and to supporting all pupils to find their particular niche in it.

Conversely, schools must be more aggressively enterprising in selling their expertise and facilities in the community. The concentration of learning spaces, learning technologies and expertise that schools represent should not be confined to the education of young people. Instead, it should be available to the whole community to power and direct regeneration and social integration.

Sadly, the community use of school assets that was once very common now has artificial barriers placed in the way of their full integration as learning hubs.

Case study

MODELS OF EXCELLENCE: VILLAGE COLLEGES AT THE HEART OF THE COMMUNITY

I was fortunate to start my teaching career in a Cambridgeshire village college. The village college tradition was the brainchild of Henry Morris in the interwar years. Cambridgeshire was a poor county at the time and, with the exception of Cambridge, mostly comprised small, isolated rural communities. Morris argued successfully for the building of village colleges as educational and social hubs to provide in the memorable phrase 'education from the cradle to the grave.'

The village college in which I taught had 750 pupils on roll. Sporting, recreational, social and leisure facilities available to the school by day, were available to the community by night and at weekends. The facilities were overseen by the community tutor. Crucially, the holder of this post held a place on the senior leadership team.

The community tutor's role was to maintain the current provision and extend the offer to new opportunities. For example, the arrival of the first computers meant that a range of adult education courses from beginner to programming was soon in place. Vocational courses from RSA typing courses to bookkeeping provided a local route to upskill or to launch new enterprises. The technology department had a full suite of lathes and milling machines. This enabled hobby-level or more serious projects to be completed with professional support. There was a car maintenance bay which formed the first experience for those who would go on to be professional mechanics, as well as a prepping station for local stock cars. It seemed as if anything could be accommodated with a little lateral thinking. The revue and drama society (Radsoc), of which a Cambridge academic was a leading light, was a thriving enterprise. Productions were wondrous community engagements, pulling in expertise from the whole village for the various tasks that make a successful drama production. This cross-fertilisation of expertise and experience enriched the whole community, both economically and socially.

Schools have many, if not all, of these facilities still and yet the perceived cost of opening to the public in the evenings appears to be a limiting factor in providing this provision; best practice is often provided by sixth form colleges who have looked to expand provision beyond the traditional school day. The problem is one of the column in which such activities are placed. If evening classes are seen as an investment, which contributes to the upskilling of the local community, it represents a better investment than the budgets of the Department for Work and Pensions for an investment in the community. Schools have the facilities to be engines of social and economic regeneration. The most important missing element is the vision to realise this potential.

What do you want to be when you leave school? Careers guidance and work placements

A similar area where there has been a retreat from almost universal provision to a lottery of mixed or absent opportunities is in the support pupils receive around careers guidance and work experience. Despite this being a statutory provision, there is now only a patchwork of providers in place. In addition, schools struggle to find their own placements, again approaching local business with a 'begging bowl' mentality.

There are costs to business in providing a meaningful work experience for pupils. Not least of these are the requirements regarding health and safety and safeguarding. Even so, these are not insurmountable problems when there are robust systems in place. Equally significant is the quality of the experience provided, the costs of ensuring positive supervision and a range of exciting tasks that put the pupil in real-world experiences. Such experiences must allow them to calculate risks and experience what the world of work requires in terms of attitudes, behaviours and competences.

It is immensely frustrating to see pupils thrown into a work experience placement towards the end of their statutory education with the wise but unspecified words: 'Don't let yourself or the school down!'

How can pupils be aware of what is required in the world of work if the school has so assiduously made sure that school-based learning is so far removed from experience in the world of work? Work placements and careers guidance both suffer from being considered a single event, rather than a cumulative, iterative process that develops from their introduction to school in Year 7.

How can any pupil in Year 11 be expected to provide a rational and considered answer to the question 'What do you want to do when you leave school?' The only job pathways with which they will be familiar will be through their parents' work, teaching, and a week spent in a local retail outlet or similar. Even worse, the potential for pupils to become an effective, self-employed person of the sort who increasingly dominates the economy is not developed through an enterprise and entrepreneurial strand at school.

In truth, this should no longer be seen as a bilateral issue between schools and industry. The young people let down by the current poor and disjointed provision deserve a voice in developing more rational, comprehensive and ambitious transition pathways from education to employment, not least because it is one of the most significant life changes they face.

Research from the Health Foundation explores the attitudes of young people going through this transition (Hagell et al, 2019). Significantly, it was commissioned by health organisations; the toll on pupils' mental health and physical well-being of poor or failed transition between education and the world of work is often paid by young people.

Working in a new collaborative relationship with all three parties, there is much that schools, young people and businesses can do to address these issues. Such solutions are low-cost and high-impact.

Curriculum collaborations

The smaller the business, the greater the cost of providing a work experience placement for pupils. However, a film crew of pupils with teacher supervision could spend half a day making a promotional video about local employers, as well as filming a problem the company faces and to which they want pupil solutions.

It might be dealing with waste, environmental improvements, reducing costs or any number of issues that could be presented to pupils as a problem that requires them to work in teams to provide a solution.

a. A tour of our organisation and how to become part of our team.

b. The challenge:
How do we recruit and retain more staff to grow our business?

Traditionally, practical problem-solving has been seen largely as the preserve of only one department in school: design and technology. In many schools, their technology elements have been sacrificed as too expensive, so they now only design rather than make solutions; a terrible indictment of the current state and direction of travel of education.

Business Partnership Challenge 174 Y10 / Tech/Art/Music/ICT

a. A tour of our organisation and how to become part of our team.

b. The challenge:
How do we build a logo, webpage, video and online advert for a new business?

Such business-sponsored, problem-solving projects introduced in increasing complexity from Year 7, would give real outlets for pupils' skills in mathematics, science, English and the creative arts. The span of industries covered could be from engineering to childcare, logistics to financial services, and public services to aviation and anything in between.

Business Partnership Challenge 114 Y7 / Science /Tech/Geography

a. A tour of our organisation and how to become part of our team.

b. The challenge:
How do we become more environmentally friendly in our production and recycling processes?

Imagine the added value if, instead of each school working independently, they all contributed to a national scheme that shared all the challenges generated across the country. Additionally, there could be opportunities to display group work, undertake research and develop presentation skills on which their future will be determined.

For the company, it means a single morning could inform 100 lessons across local schools over several years, so this system becomes cost-effective. It also gives pupils insights into their particular niche in industry so they develop a more detailed understanding of what work entails in particular enterprises. This will help pupils make more informed choices as to the type of work placements that would interest them. It might also mean offering employment opportunities to local pupils on the basis of their work experience which showed their initiative, commitment and problem-solving ability. On reflection, of all the work experience monitoring visits I undertook, I never experienced a single employer talking about a pupil's English or mathematics skills. Their focus was always about commitment, initiative and ability to learn new skills. There is a lesson for schools in this feedback.

❖ Triangulation point

1. Consider the current provision of careers advice and guidance in your school. What are the strengths, weaknesses and key areas for development?

2. Is your school represented on a local business forum such as the Chamber of Commerce and is your voice heard by the business community?

3. What support have you received from the business community in the past three years? Has it been financial, practical or related to curriculum development?

Summary

This chapter has recounted a sorry tale of lost opportunities to enrich pupils' learning through creative partnerships between schools and businesses. In truth, provision of careers guidance and advice, work placements and industry awareness was better some 20 years ago and has been allowed to wither on the vine.

The transition between the world of education and work is one of the most difficult a person faces in their life. Left to chance, it leads to missed opportunities, talent lost to the economy and a personal cost to young people in terms of poor employability and social and mental health problems. We cannot afford this waste of talent.

It is perfectly possible for schools and local business to devise simple, low-cost and high-impact ways in which to collaborate to enrich and provide excellence in the curriculum. How much better if those local collaborations became a national system of learning excellence?

further reading

Henry Morris and the Village College movement in Cambridgeshire: http://infed.org/mobi/henry-morris-village-colleges-and-community-schools/ (accessed 11 September 2019).

CBI EDUCATION AND SKILLS SURVEYS

The annual CBI education and skills survey gives the latest information about how well industry (in its widest definition) and education are collaborating. In past years, the CBI reports read like a longstanding lament on the failure of education to produce 'job ready' young people to join the labour market. It must be stressed that any deficiencies in the preparation for work were not a reflection of the young people. It was a systemic failure of schools.

In recent years, although the focus is on skill deficiencies, there is a wider commitment to joint initiatives to redress the balance. Unfortunately, they are add-on extras to the curriculum, rather than wider curriculum redesign. The CBI's broadest commitment to future learning was probably their commitment to the development of the Opening Minds curriculum model.

CBI/Pearson (2018) Educating for the Modern World. *CBI/Pearson*. [online] Available at: www.cbi.org.uk/articles/educating-for-the-modern-world/ (accessed 11 September 2019).

Bibliography

Cassidy, S (2014) School Leavers Lack Basic Work Skills, CBI Warns. *Independent*. [online] Available at: www.independent.co.uk/news/education/education-news/school-leavers-lack-basic-work-skills-cbi-warns-9582458.html (accessed 11 September 2019).

Cope, J (2018) Higher Skilled Roles Rise, As Skills Gap Grows. *CBI/Pearson*. [online] Available at: www.cbi.org.uk/media-centre/articles/higher-skilled-roles-rise-as-skills-gap-grows-cbipearson-annual-report/ (accessed 11 September 2019).

Dalby, D M (2015) *A Study of the Experiences of Vocational Students Learning Functional Mathematics in Further Education Colleges.* University of Nottingham PhD thesis. [online] Available at: http://eprints.nottingham.ac.uk/28308/1/Thesis%20final%20Dec%202014.pdf (accessed 11 September 2019).

Finegold, D and Soskice, D (1988) Education, Training and Economic Performance. *Oxford Review of Economic Policy*, 4(3): 21–53.

Guardian Letters (2019) Funding and Staff Levels in Schools at Crisis Point. *Guardian*. [online] Available at: www.theguardian.com/education/2019/mar/11/funding-and-staff-levels-in-schools-at-crisis-point (accessed 11 September 2019).

Hagell, A, Shah, R, Viner, R, Hargreaves, D, McGowan, J and Heys, M (2019) *Young People's Suggestions for the Assets Needed in the Transition to Adulthood: Mapping the Research Evidence*. Health Foundation working paper. Future Health Inquiry working paper number 2. London: Health Foundation and Association for Young People's Health. [online] Available at: www.health.org.uk/sites/default/files/upload/publications/2019/Health%20Foundation%20working%20paper%20assets%20final_v3.pdf (accessed 11 September 2019).

Hillage, J (2018) Young People Still Struggle to Thrive in Today's Labour Market. *Institute for Employment Studies*. [online] Available at: www.employment-studies.co.uk/news/young-people-still-struggle-thrive-todays-labour-market (accessed 11 September 2019).

Speckesser, S and Sala, L K (2015) *Empirical Research on Youth Transitions to, and within, the Labour Market: Education and Labour Market Trends Affecting 16-to-24 Year Olds and the Impact on Adult Employment Trajectories*. BIS Research Paper 255B. London: Department for Business Innovation and Skills. [online] Available at: https://assets.publishing.service.gov.uk/government/uploads/system/uploads/attachment_data/file/471046/BIS-15-614-Empirical-research-on-youth-transitions-to-and-within-the-labour-market.pdf (accessed 11 September 2019).

13. EVERY CHILD AN EXCELLENT LEARNER

Critical issues

» The intimate relationship between inclusion and excellence.

» The relationship between behaviours and the learning environment.

» Defining and accommodating inclusion in the school culture.

» Challenging labels: difference and diversity as strengths.

» Inclusion and the school mission statement: intent and actions.

No excellence without inclusion

While researching on the internet, I recently came across a short video from a US primary school in which a teacher was greeting pupils at the door of his classroom. They indicated on a laminated sheet stuck on the wall how they wanted to be greeted by the teacher as they entered the classroom at the start of the lesson (see Figure 13.1).

How would you like to be greeted today?

Hand shake　　　High five

Thumbs up　　　Namaste

Figure 13.1 Classroom greeting: mutual respect and learning effectiveness

My first thought was that it was rather exuberant, but then I remembered my first day at an inner city school in crisis and thought of meeting a beleaguered Year 11 class, five months from taking their examinations and having been subject to a range of supply teachers who had contained rather than taught them. In the sleepless night before meeting them, I decided that I would slow, and control, entrance to the classroom by shaking the hand of each one of them in a formal introduction, asking their name and any pet names they preferred to be known by.

It worked to the extent that the usual torrent of pupils pouring into the class was stemmed and, being disconcerted by this novel approach, I bought myself some time to explain that we had a wonderful opportunity to begin a new relationship that was going to be positive; to assure them that, unlike the supply teachers, I was here to stay and would do all I could to help them achieve the highest grades possible.

The lesson proceeded as well as could be expected, until I mentioned the word 'homework'. There was much muttering in the ranks and Grant was delegated to speak for the class. What he said was not a challenge, but a statement of fact: 'Sir, this is Bulwell. We don't do homework in Bulwell. Ever!'

I thanked the class for making this clear, but explained that if we were going to make up for lost time we would need to do homework from this point. They grudgingly made a note of the task and I was surprised to find later that they all had some work completed and ready to be peer-marked during the next lesson.

The pupils were initially suspicious, and it was Easter before Wayne casually mentioned that I was now regarded as a 'safe' teacher.

'Safe' was the highest accolade that could be paid to a teacher at this school. It was an incredibly sophisticated term comprising mutual respect, confidence in fairness and consistency. It applied to a teacher who was not averse to 'having a laugh' and who was a good communicator of learning; someone who would help individuals without making them look stupid.

Intuitively, both the greeting sheet and my stumbling efforts pointed to a universal truth in learning. That learning is a shared venture that requires mutual respect to operate effectively.

Inclusion is not just about accommodating those pupils who have diverse needs within the school environment. To be meaningful and inclusive, the school should accommodate the diversity of pupils' individual needs into the principles of every element of its operation.

I have not begun a chapter on inclusion and excellence from the point of view of special educational needs and disability provision because one layer below acknowledged and statemented disabilities are the learning needs every pupil will exhibit at various times. The pupil who has lost a parent, the pupil living hand to mouth in poor quality accommodation, pupils with emotional and mental health problems, the pupil whose education is interrupted by regular hospital stays and who feels socially isolated, or the pupil who has come to school without breakfast again – all must be recognised and accommodated if they are to become highly effective learners.

Such examples should not be seen as exceptional. Instead, they should be seen as permanent and intermittent aspects of pupils' lives. Systems should be in place to recognise, intervene and support pupils in poverty, with mental and physical health issues or family crisis, or a myriad other blocks to effective learning. Staff must be trained to recognise symptomatic behaviours and trigger appropriate support.

In a secondary school context, the dominance of subject specialist departments means teachers consider themselves first and foremost as a teacher of their subject. The unfortunate corollary of this belief is that any pupil who does not conform to the teacher's expectations in the classroom is filtered down one of two routes. This system distances the 'subject teacher' from having to address the issues themselves. They can filter pupils who do not conform in class to the tutor or head of year, thereby quarantining the issue from their classroom.

First, a pupil's behaviour might be reported to the special needs department, with an underlying suggestion that the pupil might be better off withdrawn from the class and accommodated with specialists because of their disruptive behaviour.

Second, what is seen by the subject teacher as 'challenging behaviour' is filtered down the disciplinary route. This usually occurs after the teacher has tried to cow the pupil to behave by a series of verbal threats. These escalate rapidly to the point that the teacher has run out of sanctions, while the pupil's unacceptable behaviour continues to escalate. At no point is there any recognition on the part of the subject teacher that this behaviour is an external expression of some deeper need in the pupil which is not being met in the classroom.

Once the perspective is that the pupil is 'behaving badly', the predisposition is to take the disciplinary route. However, a change in teacher perception, to recognise that the behaviour indicates an underlying need that the pupil is struggling to handle, produces a more supportive response. Unfortunately, for the second response to flourish, the teacher must have a level of self-awareness and emotional maturity that has been nurtured by training. They also need sufficient emotional investment in the well-being and success of the pupil to prioritise support over punishment.

Case study

Few people have pushed me to the end of my tether more than Ian when he was in Year 9. Lesson after lesson, he would deliberately provoke confrontation, compromise my lessons and even put his or others' safety at risk. I would use up just about all the school-based sanctions on each occasion. Finally, I decided to have a formal meeting with him. We settled down in the interview room with a cup of tea and a biscuit and I admitted I was running out of ideas to reach an accommodation whereby I could teach and he could learn. He put together a lucid set of propositions about the underlying reasons which manifested in his behaviour. He wanted to test me. He actually wanted to see at what point I would give up on him. He knew that he would have broken me once I had hit him.

This was frightening stuff. To have been so systematic in his plan of disruption showed both great intelligence and some desperate underlying experiences. This was clearly a learned behaviour. Circumstances improved marginally over time, so I was concerned when Ian opted for my subject at GCSE, thinking that we were both in for a miserable two years. I could not have been more wrong.

At GCSE level, I made great play of the fact that they had chosen my subject. We now needed to work together to decide how we were going to get them ready to give a great account of themselves in the examination. The element of negotiation of class rules and more pupil-led learning resulted in a far more relaxed and purposeful atmosphere for learning. For Ian, the change in environment led to a change in behaviour.

The relationship between behaviours and the learning environment

To use Kevin Hewitson's 'learning quotient' model (Hewitson, 2015), Ian had been given four key elements in terms of his learning needs (see Figure 13.2):

1. *Power* in the classroom by being acknowledged as a person of worth.
2. *Belonging* because he had been enlisted as a member of a learning community, rather than as a disruptive influence.
3. *Choice* as he was able to choose his behaviours and actions, and make these effective ones.
4. *Fun* as in this more relaxed and supportive atmosphere he could achieve, celebrate and feel relaxed.

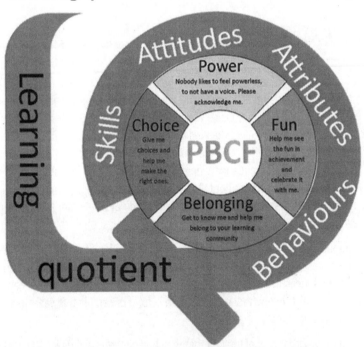

Figure 13.2 Setting a learning environment: the learning quotient approach

By kind permission of Kevin Hewitson, ace-d Advocating Creativity, 2015

Accommodating full inclusion

Having worked from the needs of the individual and the ways in which they may be accommodated in the learning environment, be this the classroom or beyond, let us consider the wider school and inclusion.

Inclusion, as a concept, is not usually universally applied to all pupils. Instead, it is one reserved for those pupils with 'special' learning needs, a physical or mental disability, and their accommodation within the wider learning community. Treating such pupils as a discrete group can be profoundly unhelpful. Working with this dichotomy of 'normal' and 'special' pupils does both groups a disservice and obscures wider learning conversations. It encourages an attitude that is 'inclusion by exception' rather than 'inclusion by principle'.

As outlined above, it often encourages teachers to regard the special needs of their pupils to be beyond their remit to address. Moreover, there were implicit assumptions made in the use of various terms for classifying special educational needs and issues of integration.

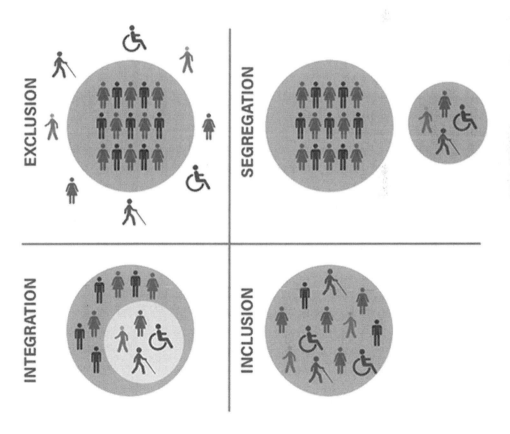

Figure 13.3 Inclusion, excellence and the importance of definitions

Figure 13.3 shows the evolution of structural provision for pupils who have special needs.

Few would now argue for exclusion as a basis of policy. Nonetheless, the increase in reports of attacks on people with learning disabilities suggests that not even this historical argument has yet been fully won. Segregation has been argued for on the basis of providing specialist provision in the concentration needed to improve the learning support required to meet the needs of pupils with learning disabilities. This argument has some merit at a technical level, but totally ignores the social costs of such a system in not allowing all pupils to integrate, thereby fostering preconceptions and misconceptions.

Integration was seen as a political commitment to equality. However, it tended to focus on the practical elements of considering structural preconditions such as accessibility and personal needs, rather than the deeper conversation about equity.

A telling analogy to illustrate the distinction between equality and equity was presented to me when I was involved in the Building Schools for the Future programme. An architect explained that to accommodate pupils in wheelchairs, they would build a ramp to the side of the main entrance stairs. A special needs teacher replied that if they abandoned the stairs and simply had a ramp, all pupils would enter the school with parity of esteem, the wheelchair users would have a sense of belonging, rather than being 'accommodated' and defined by their disability.

True inclusion comes with sizeable costs. The greatest is not the expense of architectural or structural changes in the building, but in challenging and changing the mindset of the school community to recognise that inclusion and excellence are compatible. Inclusion is a belief system that requires universal regard for learners and changes to learning models which build on every pupil's strengths. By definition, this will require the ipsative model of assessment, which aims to coach improvement from the current performance level, in order to square excellence with inclusion.

CHALLENGING LABELS: DIFFERENCE AND DIVERSITY AS STRENGTH

Thankfully, the standard and rather disjointed models of change towards embracing inclusion are being finessed by metacognitive research findings and stronger advocacy groups.

The widespread range of conditions grouped under the umbrella of 'autistic spectrum disorders' now have growing numbers of advocates who reject the deficit model of disabilities. They think more around the term 'differently abled' and point to the particular strengths associated with pupils with autistic spectrum disorders in the way they see, communicate and understand the world. They project forward these learning insights and see them as particularly beneficial for employment (Noble, 2019) (see Table 13.1).

Table 13.1 The benefits of employing an individual with autism

> - HIGH LEVELS OF CONCENTRATION AND FOCUS.
> - RELIABILITY AND DEPENDABILITY.
> - ATTENTION TO DETAIL AND ACCURACY.
> - TECHNICAL ABILITIES, SUCH AS CODING AND PROGRAMMING.
> - FACTUAL KNOWLEDGE AND EXCELLENT MEMORY.
>
> NOT ALL INDIVIDUALS WITH AUTISM WILL TICK ALL THESE BOXES.

Source: Incluzy (2019)

In particular, advocacy groups working with, and for, pupils are taking on the latest neuroscience research to argue that the 'autistic spectrum' is not a separate classification, discrete from wider human behavioural experiences, but forms one specific element within it.

To emphasise this new concept, the term 'neurodiversity' is gaining currency. As one friend of mine who has autistic spectrum disorder put it: 'We all have the same brain, it is just that mine is wired slightly differently from yours. I have capacities that you don't possess and you have capacities that I don't have.' This is a very welcome change of perceptions that should bring less heat and more light to future discussions of truly inclusive school learning.

Inclusion and the school mission statement

A large number of school mission statements contain the word 'excellence'. Fewer contain the word 'inclusive'. Yet, without the latter commitment, the former is meaningless.

Mission statements can be complex and misleading things. Some are generated by the headteacher alone, some by a combination of the headteachers, governors and senior leadership teams, fewer with reference to all the staff. It follows that if the principles of inclusion do not even extend to the staff, then there is little chance they will have a daily philosophical and operational commitment to the mission.

Where are the pupils in this statement of intent? Usually, they are the passive objects of the statement and not a vibrant element in its generation. Without a statement that is inclusive, the commitment to excellence is a statement for the few. Those who, for a variety of issues, cannot access the curriculum on offer at the school will never attain excellence in their learning. The problem lies not with the learners, but with the curriculum and culture of the school itself.

Education leaders and teachers would do well to follow the example of Albert Einstein, who said: 'I never teach my pupils; I only attempt to provide the conditions in which they can learn.'

❖ Triangulation point

1. How accommodating of differently abled pupils is your school in terms of supporting human needs, social integration, provision of support and responding to different behaviours?

2. How confident are you that your policies and practices provide adequate support for all pupils? Which areas would give you most concern?

3. How much INSET and CPD time has been devoted to the support of the individual and special educational needs of your pupils by all teachers in the past three years? Do you consider this time sufficient? Do you consider the time spent effectively in improving the learning experience of your pupils?

Summary

This chapter has challenged the traditional dichotomy of 'normal' and 'special needs' pupils as being deeply unhelpful. It has emphasised that all pupils will have special and specific learning needs intermittently. These needs might express themselves in behavioural, medical, social and economic needs which will impact on their learning.

Making inclusion and excellence compatible is aided by behavioural and metacognitive research. This shows that what once were considered aspects of a pathological condition with an indeterminate definition along a 'spectrum' might, in fact, be part of the wider human learning condition.

In their universal parity of esteem and recognition of the individual needs of all pupils, schools have a long way to go in reconfiguring themselves in the positive way that Kevin Hewitson describes quite specifically as 'child friendly' in his learning quotient model.

Further reading

Holt, J (1964) *How Children Fail*. London: Pitman Publishing Company.

John Holt is held in high regard as an author of books on the child within the school system.

He considered the factors that influenced both success and learning in school systems. Much of what caused failure by pupils in learning could be put down to the culture and practice of learning in the classroom where compliance and conformity were valued over initiative and independent learning. Sanctions for non-conformist behaviour tended to stress personal humiliation and pupils being subjected to ridicule in front of peers. This led to a hostile environment for learning, which was dominated by the teacher.

Subsequently, the range of qualities and learning tested for in summative tests was too narrow, prescriptive and without value.

Sir Ken Robinson in his TED talk of the crushing of creativity in schools came to similar conclusions about the abrasive impact of schools on the embedded genius in pre-school-aged children: www.ted.com/talks/ken_robinson_says_schools_kill_creativity#t-14682; https://en.wikipedia.org/wiki/How_Children_Fail (accessed 11 September 2019).

Bibliography

Hewitson, K (2015) Advocating Creativity. *4c3d*. [online] Available at: https://4c3d.wordpress.com/2019/07/01/closing-the-achievement-net-talk-notes-and-slides/ (accessed 11 September 2019).

Incluzy (2019) The Benefits of Employing an Individual with Autism. *Incluzy*. [online] Available at: https://incluzy.com/benefits-employing-individuals-autism/ (accessed 11 September 2019).

Noble, B (2019) Employers Turn to Workers with Autism for Talent Needs. *Detroit News*. [online] Available at: https://eu.detroitnews.com/story/business/2019/07/02/michigan-employers-autism-talent-ford-gm-dte/1476878001/ (accessed 11 September 2019).

14. PARENTS AND EXCELLENCE

PARENTS' EVENING

Well Mrs Jones, I have 27 rows of summative data to show you, and, of course, you will have seen the copious notes my colleagues have made in your daughter's exercise books. This data provides a vivid picture of a child failing in learning. However, it is too late in the year to do anything about it now, and as I won't be teaching Susan next year you will need to speak to her teachers in September about what we can do about this!

Critical issues

» The cultural change for parents between primary and secondary school experiences.

» Data, technology and communication: effective use between school and home?

» Developing the home learning environment (HLE).

» Giving compensatory support to families in need.

Parental involvement in the secondary school

In my experience, the most common perception parents report when their child starts secondary school is that the bond and intimacy of the relationship they enjoyed with their child's primary school is broken or fractured.

The social, sporting and academic occasions when they visited the primary school to discuss or celebrate achievement are greatly reduced. The relationship with a single teacher, who has a holistic view of the difficulties and successes of the child, is fragmented between a tutor and up to ten subject teachers. None of these teachers seem to carry more than a series of marks in a markbook as their knowledge base of the child, the pupil, seen maybe once a week or fortnight.

Parents have less confidence that their child is 'known' and understood. There seems less accommodation of the needs of their child and the overall structure of communication and action is more formalised and complex.

Despite these changes in the level of service provided, the child is progressing through the school at an accelerated rate with key decision points occurring in Year 9 and formal examinations at Year 11 and possibly Year 13, which will define career options and life plans.

Of course, much of this decline in perceived service could be overcome if secondary schools operated on a similar model to primary schools, with the progress of the individual pupil as an effective learner considered to be more significant than the transmission of subject content. However, few secondary schools are moving in this direction. Indeed, within the multiple academy trusts (MATs) that have largely replaced the local education authorities as providers of education, priority is given to better outcomes in the subject areas of English, mathematics and science. In-house expertise in these areas is prioritised, or bought in, with consultants trying to share the best practice across the trust in these areas. This is another example of the behaviours of teachers being focused by the demands of the centre, in this case the DfE and the inspection system. It is very difficult to develop and sustain a change culture, when all the key drivers of expectation and performance focus on such a narrow band of behaviour drivers.

Data, technology and communication

The impact of information technology on school leadership has been profound. Schools are now incredibly data rich in terms of the progress mapping of pupils. They also have avenues in email and social media to bring data to the attention of parents.

Data alone, however, is not sufficient to inform and support parents to help their children. There needs to be interpretation of trends and points of intervention, and celebration, for the raw data expressed in letters or numbers to be of value to parents. Otherwise, as in many parents' evenings, teachers are supplying summative data that reflects past performance, without giving opportunities for the data to remediate or drive better performance of the individual pupil.

However, part of the problem for these limited and unhelpful interactions also rests with the parents and governors who are prepared to tolerate these less than satisfactory interactions. Much lies in the expectations of parents, borne out of their own school experience. These include expectations that books will be marked, that there will be an annual report, homework will be set and the school uniform policy will be enforced. These traditional expectations eat up the creative time available for teachers.

Let us take the time-heavy, low-impact, process of book marking as an example. Few things could help reduce the workload burden of teachers more effectively than abandoning marking the books of secondary school pupils with annotations and developmental pointers. Even with preparation time, no secondary teacher can mark, during school time, the books of all the classes they teach each week. This means this work is taken home, eating into work–life balance. This might be justified if this method of engaging pupils in developmental conversations was effective. It is not (Hallam and Rogers, 2018).

Providing detailed feedback on a piece of work from last week between seven and 14 days later, depending on the vagaries of the timetable, will not change the learning behaviour of the pupil. Perhaps, if the next lesson allocated some time for pupils to reflect on previous developmental comments, then the effectiveness of the written feedback might improve. However, this would undermine the pace of the lesson and would assume that last week's feedback could be actioned in the context of a completely new task this week.

It is perfectly possible for the elements of pupils' work that need grading to be machine marked. Indeed, examination boards have moved in this direction in recent years. This would also mean that deviations in pupils' performance would be flagged up earlier and remedial support provided across the whole range of subjects studied. A dip in performance across the whole subject range might trigger a specific conversation, which was evidence-based, between the tutor and the parents. A dip from the expected range of performance might indicate the necessity for a more focused conversation between a subject teacher and the tutor, with parents becoming involved if the issue is not resolved within school, or the dip in performance worsens.

Machine marking, and the use of multiple-choice questions to test understanding, would give more time for teachers to spend in spoken conversations and coaching. These help the individual pupil to take the next step in their learning with confidence. This technology exists in schools and, with appropriate training, and the resolve of senior management, could be resolved tomorrow.

The home learning environment (HLE)

The area where schools could have a major impact on supporting parents to improve their child's performance is in creating the circumstances for effective learning in the home environment.

I would suggest that too much time has been spent on the virtual (VLE), managed (MLE) environments and learning platforms. Too little has been invested in developing the home learning environment (HLE).

Traditionally, speaking about the process rather than the content of learning, and particularly extending the conversation into the home, has been an area where schools have not developed. This is in spite of the massive potential of such support and development in supporting pupils' learning. Where schools address the importance of the home it tends to be in the context of the revision process at the end of Year 11. This is far too late to address the setting up of home support systems as this should be dealt with as part of induction in Year 7.

This reticence can be explained partly by an expectation that the school does not intervene in home circumstances at secondary school level. However, there is growing awareness that circumstances outside school impact greatly on pupil performance as outlined in the introduction and Chapter 1. Schools have to be reactive to the social and economic impact of almost a decade of austerity policies in terms of hungry children who are poorly clothed and who require support with personal hygiene turning up daily in class. The Department for Education figures on free school meals (FSM), used as a cipher for poverty, paint a picture of increasing numbers of children growing up in relative poverty. Underlying the FSM figures are all the attendant risks to physical and mental health which will compromise pupils' ability to learn. Taken at face value, this represents 15.4 per cent (DfE, 2019) of the school population claiming FSM. In human terms, this represents 1,259,720 children living in circumstances where their parents qualify and claim free school meals (see Figure 14.1).

Percentage of pupils eligible for and claiming free school meals, 2011–2019

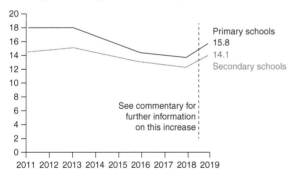

In January 2019, for all school types, 15.4 per cent of pupils were eligible for and claiming free school meals. This is the highest proportion since 2014, reversing the downward trend. Since April 2018, protections have been in place for FSM eligibility while Universal Credit is introduced nationwide. This has been the main driver in the increase in the proportion of pupils eligible for and claiming free school meals as pupils continue to become eligible but fewer pupils stop being eligible.

Figure 14.1 Free school meals data, January 2019 return

Source: DfE (2019)

Pride, the fear of stigma and not understanding the eligibility or the claims process mean that the FSM data underrepresents those children living in poverty. While in senior leadership in an inner city school we returned a figure of 49 per cent of the school population claiming FSM, and even that figure was an underrepresentation. The DfE were in contact with us immediately to say that our figure was outside the expected parameters and that we had therefore made a mistake in our calculations!

Behind these statistics is a complex picture of poverty and poor physical and mental health conditions. This has a negative impact on the ability of the whole family to survive and thrive. Kirby et al (2018) explored the wider impact of supporting a child with a learning disability on the physical, mental and emotional life of the family. They drew up the impact assessment in Figure 14.2 from a survey of 300 families with a child with a diagnosis of dyspraxia.

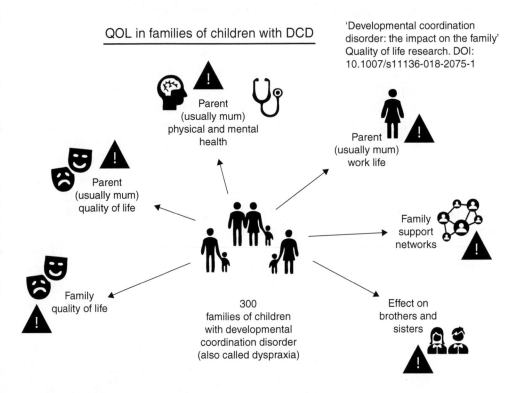

QOL in families of children with DCD

'Developmental coordination disorder: the impact on the family' Quality of life research. DOI: 10.1007/s11136-018-2075-1

Parent (usually mum) physical and mental health

Parent (usually mum) work life

Parent (usually mum) quality of life

Family support networks

Family quality of life

300 families of children with developmental coordination disorder (also called dyspraxia)

Effect on brothers and sisters

Figure 14.2 Quality of life (QOL) impact of families with children with a learning disability

Source: Kirby et al (2018)

Deprivation loves company and it tends to cluster. In the former coal-producing areas of Nottinghamshire, a culture of not valuing education persisted two generations after the pits closed. Massive regeneration initiatives in the area have created skilled and well-paid jobs, particularly in logistics. However, lacking the qualifications and experience of work, few of the local people can access them. A headteacher friend, who runs a primary school in the area, said that the paucity of aspiration in the town was epitomised by the highest term of abuse used between pupils. Those who are reserved for particular contempt are called 'jobbers' because their parents had a job in a town where the levels of social deprivation mean that employment is exceptional, and has been for two decades.

In that community, and I will argue in every other, greater engagement with the child as a learner within the home would reap massive benefits in attitude change.

Giving compensatory support to families in poverty

To counter the appalling picture of educational disadvantage produced by poverty, I propose a programme of practical support which would be proactive. It helps parents to develop the home learning environment and gives every child the conditions in which they can thrive as learners.

This support structure would require its own book, so I will only consider the key principles that should apply in the design of a home/school support package.

Of course, much of what would comprise the fundamentals of such support are already in place in the homes of children whose parents have benefited from access to higher education. Educational success for such children can be modelled by parents keen that their own children have the same opportunities they enjoyed.

For those children living in more fragile circumstances, comprising home insecurity, mental health issues, food or fuel poverty or chronic sickness, or whose parents had a poor experience with school-based learning, such support is not implicit or explicit. They are left to struggle on under the sapping weight of such burdens.

Principle 1. Recognise that the most likely reason parents are unable to support their children to develop as learners in the home is because their own educational experience was unsatisfactory. Building a programme that revisits their unhappy experience of educational failure will not yield positive results.

Principle 2. A programme built on curriculum content makes unwarranted assumptions about the ability of parents to deliver it, so the focus of the programme has to be attitudes, behaviours and competences (ABC) for positive learning.

Principle 3. Focus on the key skills of time and resource management as they represent universal elements that parents and pupils need to balance to complete any task, assignment or extended project.

Applying these three principles provides a template against which to build the key features of the home learning environment. Figure 14.3 considers these principles in a system.

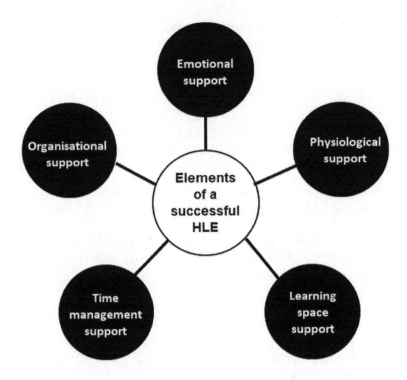

Figure 14.3 Building an effective home learning environment (HLE)

Figure 14.3 presents five aspects of the home learning environment as having equal significance, but this is not the case. One aspect is the foundation point of the whole system of support, and without it, the system will fail.

1. Emotional support

   Emotional support is the core of the whole HLE concept. It spans the whole range of human emotions from anger management to stress, and lethargy to depression. In the course of a secondary career, the pupil will have increasing demands placed on them at the very time when they are experiencing hormone surges and significant life changes. They often become less communicative in dealing with these life changes. This means the parent needs to be more proactive in seeking to share their child's life and concerns in non-threatening ways.

   Asking pupils about what happened at school today generally elicits a negative response. However, asking open-ended questions with plenty of speculations and phrases – such as 'What made you happy today?', 'Why do you feel that way?', 'Where do you think you are doing well?', 'Which areas can you improve?' – should bring greater success. Asking such questions over the dinner table has great benefits. First, their commitment to eating gives them less opportunity to disengage, and, second, using the dinner table as the place where you review the day and sort any outstanding issues makes it a very important place and time. This is recognised by anthropologists who give it the name 'commensality' and eating together is seen in many societies as the place and time to resolve differences and discuss perspectives. It is also the time to model for pupils how a mature adult tackles difficult issues by thinking them through and developing an action plan.

This is the best place to share encouragement and negotiate goals and incentives for key performance indicators. It is unwise to tie a child's performance to a financial or other benefit. The child needs to learn for intrinsic reasons such as personal satisfaction, or to work towards long-term career goals, rather than for a short-term, extrinsic reward.

The mental health of young people is currently a cause of great concern. Stress and even elements of 'feeling down', short of clinical depression, are part of the human condition. Much can be done to relieve the burden of stress by understanding the challenges the child faces, and talking through potential issues and solutions. This is, in effect, home-based talking therapies. The difficult balance is to maintain these positive conversations as the pressures on the child intensify. However, many stresses of the examination period are situational stresses, which recede once the examination period passes, and the child has had a period to decompress and return to a more balanced lifestyle. If the child enters a spiral of increasing emotional intensity, when they are is clearly not coping, despite parental support, then consulting the school and the doctor are absolute necessities.

2. Physiological support

An adolescent child requires significant physiological support as their body grows.

Adequate sleep is a critical factor in optimum functioning of the body. Irritability and failure to concentrate, factors that the child might put down to stresses of the day, are more usually associated with poor or disturbed sleep patterns. Ensuring that a child has the appropriate amount of sleep related to their age in a quiet, dark and cool room is critical to good physical and mental health.

Similarly, any teacher will tell of the impact of high energy drinks on pupil behaviour and performance in afternoon lessons. Maintaining a balanced diet, with low sugar intake, adequate roughage and vegetables, will have a positive impact on a child's ability to perform adequately.

Attention to physical exercise also plays a critical part in human performance. Ensuring that, as part of the half-hour intensive work sessions, the child has opportunities to move around, and even complete short stretching or strength-building exercises, helps to maintain concentration and challenge. Too often, as the pressures of the secondary school grow, the normal pattern of the week, including exercise and recreation, are sacrificed. Maintaining normal patterns of enjoyable exercise, and weaving work sessions between them, makes for the optimum performance.

3. Organisational support

Securing an adequate level of organisational support is as difficult as ensuring suitable emotional support. This involves having sufficient information to prompt the child to improve their organisational strategies.

There is a tendency to attempt to do too much for the child in this sphere, creating a dependency culture rather than independence. A large wall chart of key dates and plans to arrive at them well prepared, access to the school timetable and homework diary will be required here as well as equipment requirements on certain days.

Occasionally, the child must fail in a task, if only to understand that actions, or inactions, have consequences. The parental response at this point should follow the advice given in emotional support. Reactions such as 'I told you so!' are really unhelpful. Far more positive is an opportunity for the child to examine their emotional response to failure with a 'How do you feel about this?' followed by 'What can we do to make sure this doesn't happen again?'

4. Time management support

All project management is essentially time management. The quality of what can be achieved will depend on the time available. Time is exceptionally egalitarian – we all have exactly the same amount to spend. The secret is to use it effectively to get the best return on our investment.

Helping a pupil to manage time by breaking down tasks into ordered components is the secret to effective revision. The use of the half-hour time slot for tasks, and mapping progress on a large chart of what is required to achieve objectives, imposes both a discipline and a sense of purpose as sub-targets are met. This, in turn, gives the pupil a sense of control and progress which counteracts the panic that poor time management entails. Nothing is more stress-inducing than having too much to do and not enough time to complete it to the required standard.

5. Learning space support

Making the association between a purposeful space and purposeful work is often overlooked.

If there is a dedicated space devoted to work at home it makes for an easier engagement in the learning process. Without such a space, time is wasted constantly trying to settle in appropriate spaces and then finding all the materials, paper, pens, pencils and rulers required to make the space effective.

The prerequisites of the space are minimal, but significant. Emotionally, it must be a space over which the child has a sense of ownership. There needs to be a flat surface with all the materials required to hand. Working while lying on a bed, for example, is the prelude to drowsiness and wasted time. There are arguments about whether work should be conducted with music or not. I know colleagues who recommend classical music because the beat pattern of classical music is helpful to the thinking brain. Others believe total silence is a prerequisite of effective learning. I am undecided, except for suggesting that it should be the child who has the ability to control the level of sound in which they work.

Certainly other distractions, like a television, or computer game, should only be accessed for recreational use at the end of the study session. It is possible to work with background noise, but only when the work you are completing is sufficiently engrossing to enable you to block out visual or auditory distractions. It is difficult to reach that level of engagement with the work when there are competing noises distracting you. These then are some minimal considerations for supporting learning in the home environment.

❖ Triangulation point

1. How does the support for home learning your school provides compare to the minimal aspects discussed above?

2. When does such parental support appear in your planning? From Year 7 onwards, or in the run-up to the examination period?

3. Could you identify from your existing data who are the pupils and parents who would gain most from such a programme of support and how would you deliver it for maximum effectiveness?

Summary

The relationship between parents, pupils and learning excellence in school is one of missed opportunities.

We started the book with the statement that the system blights almost 80 per cent of pupils to be seen as failures in the system. This chapter has explored some of the problems that the families of such pupils have in supporting their child to learn. It showed some key deficiencies that make pupils unable, and sometimes unwilling, to gain the maximum benefit from the education on offer.

The school can identify these pupils from their management data. Yet having creative and supportive conversations with such pupils' parents, not only in Year 11 as the examination period begins but along the whole of the pupil's secondary career, could remove significant barriers to effective learning. This would make significant progress in giving them the self-management skills required to thrive beyond school.

If only schools were prepared to give equal regard to those pupils who require compensatory support to develop as learners as they do to those identified as 'gifted and talented'.

Bibliography

DfE (2019) *Schools, Pupils and Their Characteristics*. London: Department for Education. [online] Available at: https://assets.publishing.service.gov.uk/government/uploads/system/uploads/attachment_data/file/812539/Schools_Pupils_and_their_Characteristics_2019_Main_Text.pdf (accessed 11 September 2019).

Hallam, S and Rogers, L (2018) *Homework: The Evidence*. London: UCL IOE Press.

Kirby, A, Cleaton, P and Lorgelly, A (2018) Developmental Coordination Disorder: The Impact on the Family. *Journal: Quality of Life Research*, 4.

15. CONCLUSION

Critical issues

» Misdirection of a national system of education.

» The thinking school: deconstructing learning and rebuilding for the education of the future.

» Excellence, inclusion and the learner in the school of the future.

A national system unfit for purpose

This book is based on 40 years' involvement in education. When I started to write it, I thought I had a clear overview of what I wanted to share. This was based on experiences, collaborations and brilliant practice I have witnessed, and conversations with people I consider to be at the leading edge of the evolution of learning. The tone of the book was meant to be developmental, to highlight some structural impediments to effective learning. These needed to be addressed to make excellence the characteristic demonstrated by each and every pupil.

This commitment to a gradualist and developmental tone did not survive the first chapter.

I made a statement that the current system, in its pursuit of excellence, neglected the learning needs of a large majority of school pupils. The system is geared to pursuing the aspirations of the top 20 to 30 per cent of pupils who are considered for entrance into the higher education sector. It was meant to be a provocation, a proposition around which I could build an effective call for the review of some elements of current practice in English secondary schools.

The more I considered it, the more the statement seemed outrageous. Therefore, I had a number of discussions with former colleagues and collaborators in the UK and internationally, hoping to find a less combative starting point. Those conversations revealed that perhaps even my statement was too tame in its scope.

It is not features of the English education system that need reform. Rather, it is the whole foundation, structures and direction of travel.

Section A explores the dimensions in which the school operates and is responsive to national, local and sectional interests. The conclusion of these explorations regarding the external drivers of the school were stark.

We appear to be using a school cultural outlook frozen in the year 1955 to teach a constipated curriculum model of redundant information that had its origins in the nineteenth century, using a pattern of the school year firmly rooted in the agrarian economy of the nineteenth century and the ecclesiastic calendar that extended back to the early Christian era.

What are seen as educational impediments to the consistency of progress for pupils, such as the long summer holiday, which disrupts the learning of all pupils and the less advantaged ones even more significantly, are treated as sacred cows. Where research demonstrates the negative impact of this long learning discontinuity, tradition argues for its retention, in some cases as recuperation time for teachers!

Five school terms, each of eight weeks, with two-week breaks between them and a shorter summer break would be a much more educationally sound proposition as the RSA Academy has demonstrated in its calendar. However, the more likely trigger in parents' and teachers' attitudes to achieve such change might be that it would free them from the most expensive time to take a holiday, rather than regard for a learning argument.

The recipients of this tired and misguided educational model will be a generation of young people who, by dint of our past actions, face an existential crisis on two fronts: political and environmental. Both need to be addressed and ameliorated in the span of their lifetimes.

If we are to overcome these joint crises, and others that stem from them, we cannot afford to waste the talents of a single person.

Massive cultural change in the education system is coming. It is increasingly unfit for purpose, and no amount of tinkering with the superstructure of the curriculum content will overcome the crumbling of the foundations. Schools are driven by the behaviours of key people. The behaviours are driven by the cultural norms and the incentives and penalties in the system.

Currently, schools are working at an increasing pace, using a quality-control system that focuses on failing many/most pupils in the pursuit of delivering success for those deemed qualified to enter higher education. This system employs assessment systems which do not engage pupils and which may alienate them from learning. Nor does the system promote development of 'how to learn' strategies that underpin the development of effective independent and autonomous learners who can work beyond school on real-time, real-life problem-solving. Moreover, the curriculum diet on offer is largely simulation-based with few opportunities to test knowledge and understanding in a context beyond school. Pupils have limited opportunities to engage with significant players and organisations beyond the walls of the 'monastic school'.

Vocational pathways, careers guidance and work experiences which will shine a light on the world of work that the majority of pupils will enter straight from school are limited by paucity of understanding and lack of funding. It is a national disgrace that the universal provision of quality-assured work experience available through partnering the schools, the education/business partnerships and the Training and Enterprise Council 20 years ago is now a dissipated, underfunded system with little coherence.

In this system, teachers' professional expertise is marginalised to the latest government policy announcement. Schools are expected to manage a growing school population while also juggling with year-on-year budget cuts.

These practices account for the crisis in recruitment and retention. They also account for the scandal of the learned behaviour of 'off-rolling' pupils from school registers when their examination performance threatens to compromise the reputation of the school.

No school mission statement declaring 'excellence and inclusion' is worth the embossed paper on which it is printed if pupils in the school are cast adrift during the course of their secondary careers because of perceived reputational damage to the school. Similarly, there may be the financial advantage of keeping the pupil on roll until funding comes in, keeping the funding and then excluding the pupil.

CONCLUSION

Layers of change: deconstructing learning for the education of the future

The education system in any country is an ecosystem of its own, with relationships, dependencies and conditions required for it to thrive. There is considerable dysfunction in the English school system because government has had too much say in the direction of travel and pace of educational change in schools, and professional educators too little. Compare this with the balance between the state and professional educators in Finland and Singapore. Although there is national debate about the purpose of education and its link to national prosperity, the fine content of the curriculum and all the delivery mechanisms are left to the professional judgement of teachers to implement.

Progressive and highly effective states, as judged by the OECD annual reports, are moving away from a subject to a skills- and project-based learning model and broader assessment models that generate a clearer picture of a pupil's achievements.

In the UK generally, and England specifically, the dominance of a content-heavy curriculum is seen as the guarantor of excellence, because it is detailed and has 'rigour'. In fact, it accelerates knowledge transfer teaching models to ensure coverage of the curriculum – pupils' understanding of concepts is superficial. Knowledge-transfer models of teaching tend to reinforce the continuation of, and preference for, teacher exposition because it is seen as more efficient than letting the pupils explore the content and come to their own conclusions.

There is no longer a commitment to a 'broad and balanced' curriculum to ensure pupils gain access to practical, vocational and creative experiences to broaden the breadth and depth of their understanding and expression. The idea that an education should comprise 'a thousand memorable moments' which would equip a young person to be flexible, adaptable and compassionate has been sacrificed to one hundred thousand gobbets of unrelated and questionable pieces of information.

There is no recognition that those one hundred thousand gobbets of information, communicated so assiduously over a pupil's educational career, are available on demand from any internet-connected search engine. The future lies not in information, that is ubiquitous. Instead, it lies in the ability to interrogate, evaluate and synthesise information into arguments, proposals and solutions to problems. To quote Henry Adams: 'They know enough who know how to learn.'

Excellence and inclusion in the individual school

Section B of the book departed from the sorry macro-level picture of the English educational system and focused on the possibilities for generating better learning outcomes in an individual school. This represents a change from what might be considered a telescopic to a microscopic perspective.

It is realised that in squaring excellence and inclusion at the level of the individual school, leadership teams and governors need to reconcile their actions with the national levers of education. They also have to satisfy the inspection process that they are maintaining learning momentum and meeting the national quality control measures.

Section B places great emphasis on relationships and partnership working to build new expectations and enhanced learning outcomes for pupils.

It shows how the relationship between the teacher, the pupil and learning can be regenerated by a clearer and forward-facing definition of the purpose of education and learning in the twenty-first century. Having a vision of the learner of the future is a required starting point, for learning cannot be a process inculcated in school and then abandoned at the end of statutory education.

Whereas many consider that preparing pupils for a turbulent and uncertain future is impossible, it is, in fact, relatively simple with the right perspective.

It is impossible if we are filling the pupil with increasingly redundant knowledge. It is far easier if we are helping them to shape the future with appropriate attitudes, behaviours and competences to be flexible and adaptable.

This preparation is impossible if we are using a pedagogy dominated by teacher exposition which disengages pupils. It is achievable if you shift the focus of learning onto a more pupil-engaged form of learning – a heutagogical model. In this, choice and independent and autonomous learning with an emphasis on extended assignments, including project-based learning, flourishes.

It is impossible if we apply an assessment system that measures the relative failure of pupils to meet an externally generated and validated set of criteria of numbers or letters. It is possible if we apply ipsative assessment criteria, which measure a pupil's performance against their own previous personal best and which, in conversation with the teacher coach, generate benchmarks, targets and new performance demands which are clear and meaningful to that specific pupil.

Such preparation is impossible if the teacher is engaged on a whistle-stop tour of a content-heavy curriculum. This model provides no time for significant thinking about the quality of what is being offered to pupils. It becomes possible when teachers are encouraged to be experimental and reflect on the qualities and tactics which generate successful learning and abandon approaches that do not work.

The most valuable asset the school has to ensure the success of its mission is the expertise of its teachers. INSET and CPD activities should focus on giving them the maximum development time to focus on their successful practice and acknowledge and eliminate ineffective approaches. Foremost of these will be the marking of books as this is probably the most ineffective and costly method of providing learners with useful developmental feedback.

It is impossible if the learning undertaken in school is based on simulation, book-based exercises that have no relationship to the world beyond the school gates and towards making a practical impact on the world. It is possible if the local community, businesses and organisations have a symbiotic relationship with school-based learning. Learning then has meaning for pupils. It generates and implements solutions to problems and builds alliances. It has a positive impact on the regeneration of the local community through improving the employability and capacity of pupils to enhance enterprise and initiative.

Preparing pupils for an effective future is impossible if your school has a fractured structure for managing the learning needs of pupils. It is possible if the school has a universal view of the expectations of pupils' development and structures, support and interventions for those with high, medium and intermittent need for additional learning support.

It is impossible if secondary schools keep parents at arm's length from the learning journey of their child. It is eminently possible if parents are better informed and able to create a positive and supportive home learning environment which promotes consistently each pupil's learning experience in school.

All these possible approaches can be developed purposefully by a school that prioritises quality assurance, ensuring resources are deployed so all pupils achieve their development targets. This is preferable to the employment of a quality control model that only fails pupils along the learning continuum.

It takes courage and determination to abandon the accepted and expected pathway, but discontinuity is the engine of breakthrough. As we know, the motor car did not come about from the linear development of the horse and cart!

To promote some discontinuous experimentation, I finish with some quotes from quality thinkers through the ages who have a clearer vision than most about what comprises quality learning.

Artificial intelligence (AI) is developing rapidly. The implications of a machine able to deliver a complete, personalised and challenging series of learning experiences in an intuitive and interactive way could be no more than a generation away. If we use the span of a generation in the development of the internet as being no more than ten years, then within a decade, much of what we consider to be the role of the teacher could be redundant. A teacher who never tires, completes marking on time, is never ill and does not falter from promoting learning to each pupil at an appropriate level looks like a winning learning proposition. Teachers are not immune from a future in which their skills are redundant. Commentators like Naval Ravikant (2017) have already foreseen such developments as a liberating experience for learners: '*A generation of auto-didacts, educated by the internet and leveraged by technology, will eventually starve the industrial-education system.*'

One way or another, the future belongs to learners. Whether the school in its current form will be the statutory place of statutory education remains to be seen.

RE-EXAMINING SUCCESS

Finally, for all the teachers, parents, leaders and learners who may stumble across this book...

Act as if what you do makes a difference. It does.

William James (nd)

Bibliography

Ravikant, N (2017) *The Knowledge Project*. [online] Available at: https://fs.blog/wp-content/uploads/2017/02/Naval-Ravikant-TKP.pdf (accessed 11 September 2019).

James, W (nd) Wikiquotes. [online] Available at: https://en.wikiquote.org/wiki/William_James (accessed 11 September 2019).

INDEX

INDEX